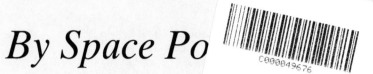

By Space Po

ARTHUR C. CLARKE

VICTOR GOLLANCZ

LONDON

First published in Great Britain 1993
by Victor Gollancz
A Cassell imprint
Villiers House, 41/47 Strand, London WC2N 5JE

© Arthur C. Clarke 1993

Material is reproduced from previously published works by ACC as follows: Chapters 1, 11, 17, 20, 21, 25: *Voices from the Sky*, Victor Gollancz, 1966; Chapter 2: *The Exploration of Space* and *Interplanetary Flight*, Temple Press, 1951, 1950 respectively; Chapters 3, 24: *The Challenge of the Spaceship*, Frederick Muller, 1960; Chapters 4, 12, 23: *1984: Spring*, Granada Publishing, 1984; Chapters 5, 6, 7: 'Beyond Apollo', the Epilogue from *First on the Moon*, Michael Joseph, 1970; Chapters 8, 9, 22: *Beyond Jupiter – The Worlds of Tomorrow* (with Chesley Bonestell), New York: Little Brown, 1972; Chapters 10, 13–16: *Report on Planet Three*, Victor Gollancz, 1972; Chapters 18, 19: *The View from Serendip*, Victor Gollancz, 1978.

All rights reserved. No part of this publication may be reproduced or transmitted in any form or by any means, electronic or mechanical including photocopying, recording or any information storage or retrieval system, without prior permission in writing from the publishers.

A catalogue record for this book is available from the British Library

ISBN 0 575 05596 0

GLOUCESTERSHIRE
CLASS
COPY
COUNTY LIBRARY
SUBJECT SPECIALISATION

Typeset at The Spartan Press Ltd,
Lymington, Hants
Printed in Great Britain by
St Edmundsbury Press Ltd,
Bury St Edmunds, Suffolk

By Space Possessed

Also by Arthur C. Clarke

Fiction

REACH FOR TOMORROW
THE OTHER SIDE OF THE SKY
A FALL OF MOONDUST
TALES OF TEN WORLDS
DOLPHIN ISLAND
THE DEEP RANGE
THE CITY AND THE STARS
THE LION OF COMARRE
THE WIND FROM THE SUN
OF TIME AND STARS
RENDEZVOUS WITH RAMA
IMPERIAL EARTH
THE FOUNTAINS OF PARADISE
THE GHOST FROM THE GRAND BANKS
THE HAMMER OF GOD

Non-Fiction

PROFILES OF THE FUTURE
VOICES FROM THE SKY
REPORT ON PLANET THREE
THE VIEW FROM SERENDIP
ASTOUNDING DAYS
HOW THE WORLD WAS ONE

by Arthur C. Clarke and Gentry Lee

CRADLE
RAMA II
THE GARDEN OF RAMA
RAMA REVEALED (Forthcoming)

by Arthur C. Clarke and Gregory Benford

AGAINST THE FALL OF NIGHT/BEYOND THE FALL OF NIGHT

(For a fuller list of other books by Arthur C. Clarke see page 222)

WITHDRAWN

990566188 3

Contents

Introduction

As I do not feel much older (or for that matter wiser) than when I started writing, I am more than a little astonished to discover that it is now sixty years since my first appearance in print. During that time I have published approximately equal quantities of fiction and non-fiction, including about a hundred essays which were collected in the volumes *The Challenge of the Spaceship* (1960), *Voices from the Sky* (1966), *Report on Planet Three* (1972), *The View from Serendip* (1978), and finally *1984: Spring*, with its self-referential publication date.

In addition, I was privileged to contribute the Epilogue, 'Beyond Apollo', to the official history, *First on the Moon* (Little, Brown, 1970), and a few years later provided the text to Chesley Bonestell's paintings of the outer solar system, *Beyond Jupiter* (Little, Brown, 1972). These two books, together with the earlier *Interplanetary Flight* (1950) and *The Exploration of Space* (1951) may be regarded as my *Summa Astronautica*.

As all these volumes are now virtually unavailable, the time seemed ripe to go through them and make a search for any pieces worth reprinting. Though such material has been dated by the course of events, this often makes them even more interesting, as a reminder of the incredible rate of scientific development during the last half-century – and the perils of prediction.

In the closing years of man's last Earthbound era, I ended a precursor to this book with the words:

Across the gulf of centuries, the blind smile of Homer is turned upon our age. Along the echoing corridors of time, the roar of the rockets merges now with the creak of the wind-taut rigging. For somewhere in the world today, still unconscious of his destiny, walks the boy who will be the first Odysseus of the Age of Space.

Who could have dreamed, when I wrote that back in 1959, that the 'boy' was then already nearing his thirtieth birthday? But there will be other Odysseys to come . . .

I am grateful to my friend John Burke for selecting the essays in this book and doing the necessary editing. Except where otherwise stated, all the contents of this volume are in my own words. Where the editor has added a note or footnote, he has initialled this (JB).

The once-ominous date 1984 seemed a good cut-off point for this book, especially as it marked – near enough – my first half-century as an author. For according to my indefatigable bibliographer Professor David Samuelson (see *Arthur C. Clarke: A Primary and Secondary Bibliography*, G. K. Hall, 1984) my first appearance in print was in the *Huish Magazine* for autumn 1932. It was at Huish's Grammar School (now Richard Huish College), Taunton, that I began to write sketches and short stories under the influence of its English master, Captain E. B. Mitford. A third of a century later, I was able to repay something of my debt by dedicating *The Nine Billion Names of God* to 'Mitty, my first editor'.

I can still recall the editorial sessions back in the early 1930s. About once a week, after class, Mitty would gather his schoolboy staff together, and we would all sit around a table on which there was a large bag of toffees. Bright ideas were rewarded instantly: Mitty invented positive reinforcement years before B. F. Skinner. He also employed a heavy metre rule for *negative* reinforcement, but this was used only in class – never, so far as I recall, at editorial conferences.

The *Huish Magazine* eventually published a dozen items of mine, totalling several thousand words. Most of these pieces were only of ephemeral interest (if that), being full of topical allusions which probably no living person, including the author, can now identify. However, even in those days my extraterrestrial interests were obvious, as will be seen from the following letter from 'Ex-Sixth-Former' stationed at a torrid and high-altitude Outpost of Empire: Vrying Pan, British Malaria. If it sounds like a run-down Moon Base, that is hardly a coincidence:

It is almost impossible to keep any liquid except under enormous pressure. However, with the powerful refrigerating plant at the rubber mines here, it is possible to reduce water to its boiling point, which is a great convenience to us in the hot weather.

The precautions we have to take to preserve our lives are extraordinary. Our houses are built on the principle of the Dewar vacuum flask, to keep out the heat, and the outsides are silvered to reflect the sunlight . . . We have to take great care to avoid cutting ourselves in any way, for if this happens our blood soon boils and evaporates.

Electricity is very cheap here, as we have got large supplies from the thermocouples. The hot end is in the sun, and the cold terminal in the boiler room in the mines, which is the coolest place in Vrying Pan.

However, I must leave off now as my ink has evaporated, in spite of the water-cooled jacket of my fountain pen.

And in 1934, believe it or not, the *Huish Magazine* published my first movie outline (Stanley Kubrick, please note), 'Jules gets His' – Shakespeare's *Julius Caesar,* transported to contemporary Chicago. I hope no copies survive . . .

Despite occasional flirtations with TV, I have found time in the last decade to produce at least a hundred thousand words of additional non-fiction, usually in connection with special events such as scientific conferences or satellite link-ups. None of this material has yet been collected into a single volume: if all goes well (to quote NASA's favourite mantram) it will appear in due course under the title *The Colours of Infinity*.

Arthur C. Clarke
Colombo, Sri Lanka
1 September 1992

— 1 —

Memoirs of an Armchair Astronaut (Retired)

This personal reminiscence first appeared in Holiday *magazine for May 1963 – six years before the first Moon landing. Fortunately the prediction in the opening paragraph was fulfilled on 20 July 1969 . . .*

For my money, the heroic period of the space age lay between 1935 and 1955; what's happened since has had a slight air of anticlimax. True, men have now actually set foot on the Moon, but today everyone takes a little thing like that for granted, and eminent scientists no longer rise in their wrath to denounce rocketeers as irresponsible crackpots. The only arguments about space that one hears today are of this type: Should Brobdingnag Astrodynamics or Consolidated Aerospace be awarded the $326,709,163 contract for the first-stage Mastodon booster?

It was all very different in the pre-war years, when the annual income of the British Interplanetary Society was about a hundred pounds. (I should know; as treasurer, I had the terrifying responsibility of accounting for it.) On the other side of the Atlantic, the American Rocket Society was slightly more affluent, but as we both operated with a part-time, volunteer secretarial staff, contact between our two organizations was erratic. In those days, moreover, the BIS and the ARS were divided by an ideological gulf, long since bridged.

As is well known, we British are a romantic and wildly imaginative race, and to our annoyance the conservative Americans did not consider that space travel was respectable. Though they had formed the American Interplanetary Society in 1930, the name had been changed to American Rocket Society a few years later. The suggestion was sometimes made that we should follow suit, but we refused to lower our sights. To us, the rocket was merely the interplanetary bus; if a better one came along (it hasn't yet, but we're still hoping) we would transfer, and give the rocket back to the fireworks industry.

Picture us then, in the mid-1930s, when only a few aircraft had flown at the staggering speed of three hundred miles an hour, trying to convince a sceptical world that men would one day travel to the Moon. There were about ten of us in the hard core of the society, and we met at least once a week in cafés, pubs, or each others' modest flats. We were almost all in our twenties, and our occupations ranged from aeronautical engineer to civil servant, from university student to stock exchange clerk. Few of us had technical or scientific educations, but what we lacked in knowledge we made up in imagination and enthusiasm. It was, I might add, just as well that we were over-optimistic. If we had even dreamed that the price of the first round-trip ticket to the Moon would be ten billion dollars per passenger, and that spaceships would cost many times their weight in gold, we should have been much too discouraged to continue our quarter-million-mile uphill struggle.

The total amount spent on the British space effort before the outbreak of war was less than a thousand pounds. What did we do with all that money? Let me tell you.

Most of us talked, some of us calculated, and a few of us drew – all to considerable effect. Slowly there emerged the concept of a space vehicle which could carry three men to the Moon and bring them back to Earth. It had, even for a 1938 spaceship, a number of unconventional features, though most of them are commonplace today, and many have been 'rediscovered' by later workers. Notable was the assumed use of solid propellants, of the type now employed in Polaris and similar missiles. Our first plans, based on highly unrealistic assumptions, envisaged making the entire round trip in a single vehicle, whose initial weight we hopefully calculated at about a thousand tons. (The advanced Saturns developed by NASA weigh several times as much). Later, we discussed many types of rendezvous and space-refuelling techniques, to break down the journey into manageable stages. One of these involved the use of a specialized 'ferry' craft to make the actual lunar landing, while the main vehicle remained in orbit. This, of course, was the approach later used in the Apollo Project – and I am a little tired of hearing it described as a new discovery. For that matter, I doubt if we thought of it first; it is more than likely that the German or Russian theoreticians had worked it out years before.

There is a vast gulf, almost unimaginable to the layman, between thinking of an idea, and then converting it into detailed engineering blueprints. There is an equally great gulf between the blueprints and the final hardware, so we cannot claim too much credit for our pioneering insight. Yet I am often struck by the fact that there is hardly a single new conception in the whole field of current space research; everything that is happening now was described, at least in outline, twenty or even fifty years ago.

But back to our Model T. As soon as we had finished the drawings, we published them in the minute *Journal of the British Interplanetary Society*. It took us some time to collect enough money to pay the printer; he was a Greek, I remember, and a few Hellenic spellings slipped through my proofreading. Nor am I likely to forget the day when I collected the entire edition, in two parcels, and was walking home with it to the flat I shared with another space enthusiast a few streets east of the British Museum. I had got half-way when two polite gentlemen in mackintoshes tapped me on the shoulder, and said, 'Excuse me, sir, but we're from Scotland Yard. Could we see what you have in those packets?'

It was a reasonable request, for at the time wild Irishmen were blowing up post offices to draw attention to their grievances, and the Yard was trying to round them up. (They did catch a brat named Brendan Behan, I believe.) To the considerable disappointment of the detectives, I was not even carrying *Tropic of Capricorn*, but when I presented them with copies of the journal they very gamely offered to pay. Tempting though it was to acquire a genuine subscriber (the cash box held about two pounds at the time), I refused the contribution; but I got them to carry the parcels the rest of the way for me.

The journal attracted a surprising amount of attention and a not surprising amount of amusement. That doyen of scientific publications, the good, grey *Nature*, condescended to notice our existence but concluded its review with the unkind cut, 'While the ratio of theorizing to practical experimentation is so high, little attention will be paid to the activities of the British Interplanetary Society.'

That was a quite understandable comment, but what could we do about it, with that two pounds in the till? Why, launch an appeal for an Experimental Fund.

We did so, and the money came rolling in. There was one occasion, I now blush to recall, when I shared sardines on toast with an elderly lady member in an Oxford Street tearoom and convinced her that, for fifty pounds, one could solve the basic problems of building a meteorological rocket. Eventually we rounded up a couple of hundred pounds, and the research programme was under way. (At Peenemünde, though we were not to know it for quite a while, von Braun was already heading for his first hundred million.)

All this money was something of a responsibility; having appealed for it, we had to use it, in a manner most calculated to produce both scientific results and publicity. The actual building and launching of rockets was frowned upon, for it would only result in police proceedings under the 1875 Explosives Act, as a group of experimenters in the north country had already proved.

We were in the position of someone who couldn't afford a car, but had enough for the speedometer and the rear-view mirror. This analogy is quite exact; though we couldn't make a down payment on even a compact spaceship, we felt we could develop two of the instruments needed to operate it.

It was a sensible decision, and indeed about the only one possible in the circumstances. The first project we tackled was a spaceship speedometer which had been invented by Jack Edwards, the eccentric genius who headed our research effort.

Edwards, who is now dead, was a short, bearded and excitable Welshman – and the nearest thing to a mad scientist I have ever met outside fiction. He was the director of a very small electronics firm, which soon afterwards expired thanks to his assistance; but he had an altogether uncanny grasp of the principles of astronautics. He had invented, back in 1938, what is now called inertial guidance – the technique which allows a rocket to know just where it is, and how fast it is going, by continually keeping track of the accelerations acting upon it.

Edwards' space speedometer consisted of a large aluminium disc, pivoted on ball bearings, and with sundry gears, weights and springs attached to it. As the device was moved up or down, the weights would 'sense' the forces acting upon them, and the rotation of the disc would record the distance moved. We had planned to test the gadget on one of the deeper lifts of the London Underground but, you will not be surprised to learn, it never got as far as that. The theory of the device was perfectly sound, and something similar steers every satellite into orbit today. But the engineering precision demanded was utterly beyond our means, and Mrs Edwards put her foot down on hearing of our intention to cast lead weights in her best saucepan.

Balked on the speedometer front, we tried our luck with the rear-view mirror. To keep it on course during take-off, and to provide the crew with artificial gravity, we had proposed to spin our spaceship like a rifle bullet. (The spin would be imparted by water jets, as the ship floated in a kind of raft before launching.) Even though the rate of rotation was quite low, it would obviously be impossible to take observations of the stars from our cosmic carousel, so we had to invent an optical system to unscramble the ship's spin.

This required no great originality, for the astronomers (who also look out at the stars from a spinning vehicle, the planet Earth) had solved the problem years before. Their answer is an instrument called a coelostat, which, however, has to cope with only one revolution every twenty-four hours. We built a similar arrangement of four mirrors – two fixed, two spinning – and I sacrificed the spring motor of my gramophone to provide the motive power.

The coelostat worked; it was the only thing we ever made that did. Its public demonstration took place in most auspicious surroundings, the hallowed halls of the South Kensington Science Museum, whose director deserves much credit for providing hospitality to such a far-out organization as ours. Next to the room where we held our meeting was the original Wright biplane, still in exile from the United States; on the floor above was an even more momentous piece of machinery – the 'atom smasher' with which Cockcroft and Walton had produced the first artificial nuclear reaction in 1932.

Our set-up was simple, but effective. At one side of the room was a disc with lettering on it, spinning too rapidly for the words to be read. At the other was the coelostat – a wooden box measuring about a foot each side, looking rather like the result of a *mésalliance* between a periscope and an alarm clock. When you peered through the coelostat at the spinning disc, the latter appeared to be quite stationary and you could read the inscription BIS painted on it. If you looked at the rest of the room, however, it appeared to be revolving rapidly; this was not recommended for any length of time.

Though our experimental efforts were unimpressive, we made ourselves known through countless lectures, newspaper interviews and argumentative letters to any publications that would grant us hospitality. One controversy ran for months in the correspondence columns of the BBC's weekly, *The Listener*; if we could not convince our critics, we usually routed them.

Looking back on it, I am amazed at the half-baked logic that was used to attack the idea of space flight; even scientists who should have known better employed completely fallacious arguments to dispose of us. They were so certain that we were talking nonsense that they couldn't be bothered to waste sound criticism on our ideas.

My favourite example of this is a paper which an eminent chemist presented to the British Association for the Advancement of Science. He calculated the energy that a rocket would need to escape from the Earth, made a schoolboy howler in the second line, and concluded, 'Hence the proposition appears to be basically impossible.' But that was not enough: he could not resist adding, 'This foolish idea of shooting at the Moon is an example of the absurd lengths to which vicious specialization will carry scientists working in thought-tight compartments.' I cannot help feeling that the good professor's compartment was not merely thought-tight; it was thought-proof.

As another example of the sort of stick that was used to beat us, I might mention an article that appeared under the eye-catching title 'We Are Prisoners of Fire'. This was based on the fact, deduced from radio measurements, that there are layers in the upper atmosphere where the temperature reaches a couple of thousand degrees Fahrenheit. Therefore, the writer announced, any space vehicle would melt before it got more than a few hundred miles from Earth. He had overlooked the point that, at the altitudes concerned, the air is so tenuous that the normal concept of temperature has no meaning, and one could freeze to death for all the heat that the few 2,000-degree molecules of nitrogen and oxygen could provide.

I must admit that we thoroughly enjoyed our paper battles. We knew that we were riding the wave of the future; as T. E. Lawrence said in *Seven Pillars of Wisdom*, 'It felt like morning, and the freshness of the world-to-be intoxicated us.' But the world-to-be was moving inexorably, unmistakably towards war. I remember sending out, from the third-floor flat in Gray's Inn Road that was both my residence and the BIS headquarters, an emotional farewell to all our hundred members, and then descending to the shelters as the sirens gave their warning.

But it was a false alarm; nothing happened then, or for a long time afterwards. Finding to our surprise that we had not all been blown to pieces, we resumed contact and continued our discussions, by means of correspondence and occasional private meetings. As an RAF instructor, I was in a position to indoctrinate hundreds of hapless airmen, and made the most of the opportunity. For some odd reason, my service nickname was 'Spaceship'.

At last it was winter 1944. The European conflict was clearly drawing to an end – but though there was nothing about it in the papers, for several weeks large holes had been suddenly appearing in southern England. Despite this, we were holding a meeting in London to plan our post-war activities. The speaker had just returned from a mission in the United States, where a well-known authority had assured him that tales of large German war rockets were pure propaganda. We were still laughing at this when – CRASH! – the building shook slightly, and we heard that curious, unmistakable rumble of an explosion climbing backwards up the sky, from an object that had arrived faster than the sound of its own passage . . . A few months later, when we knew his address, we hastened to confer the honorary fellowship of the society on Dr Wernher von Braun.

The post-V2 world, of course, took us much more seriously. Few people now doubted that rockets could travel great distances into space, and most were prepared to admit that men could travel with them. We had to alter our propaganda line; it was no longer necessary to spend all our efforts proving that space flight was possible – now we had to demonstrate that it was desirable. Not everyone agreed with us.

One who did was George Bernard Shaw, who joined the society in his ninety-first year and remained a member until his death. He was a personal capture of whom I was very proud; in 1946, while still at college, I sent him a copy of my philosophical, Toynbee-inspired paper 'The Challenge of the Spaceship'. To my surprise, back came one of the famous pink postcards, followed soon afterwards by a longer communication containing some typically Shavian theories of transonic flight. If you are interested, you will find the whole of the brief Shaw–Clarke correspondence in *The Virginia Quarterly Review* for winter 1960.

Less sympathetic to our aims was Dr C. S. Lewis, author of two of the very few works of space fiction that can be classed as literature, *Out of the Silent Planet* and *Perelandra*. Both of these fine books contained attacks on scientists in general, and astronauts in particular, which aroused my ire. I was especially incensed by a passage in *Perelandra* referring to 'little rocket societies' that hoped to spread the crimes of mankind to other planets. And at the words, 'The destruction or enslavement of other species in the universe, if such there are, is to these minds a welcome corollary', I really saw red.

An extensive correspondence with Dr Lewis led to a meeting in a famous Oxford pub, the Eastgate. Seconding me was my friend, Val Cleaver, a space buff from way back (and later chief engineer of the Rolls-Royce Rocket Division). Supporting Lewis was Professor J. R. R. Tolkien, whose trilogy *The Lord of the Rings* created a considerable stir a few years ago. Needless to say, neither side converted the other, and we refused to abandon our diabolical schemes of interplanetary conquest. But a fine time was had by all, and when, some hours later, we emerged a little unsteadily from the Eastgate, Dr Lewis's parting words were, 'I'm sure you're very wicked people – but how dull it would be if everyone was good.'

The post-war years brought a new and novel problem which is still with us, though in less virulent form. From 1948 onward, as you will doubtless recall, the sky started to fill with flying crockery; there were times when hardly a day went by without press reports of visitors from space. We were, obviously, the last people to deny this possibility; but we were quite sure that the arrival of genuine spaceships from elsewhere could no more be kept secret than the presence of a hungry *Tyrannosaurus rex* in St James's Park.

The Flying Saucers caused us considerable embarrassment and annoyance, because there was a danger that in the public eye we should be associated with the cranks and crackpots who were spearheading the cult. In an attempt to strike a blow for sanity, I did a half-hour TV programme exposing a gentleman who claimed to have made contact with Saucerites. My quest for ammunition led me to a second meeting with Scotland Yard, whose photographic experts examined the crudely faked 'evidence' and gave me some useful unofficial advice. I promptly returned to my own darkroom and produced a much better set of flying saucers, which proved conclusively that (a) any number can play and (b) the original photographer had been careless, because some of his saucers were clearly inside his telescope tube.

Though the society still had no money, it was a good deal larger than in the pre-war days, and the quality of its membership considerably more impressive. Our bi-monthly journal was widely read; in particular, the Soviet embassy subscribed to twenty copies. And here is a very odd thing; though the Russians purchased the journal in bulk and arranged their own distribution, they sent us a complete list of all the scientific and technical institutions in the USSR which received copies. We would never have dreamed of asking for such a document, but it arrived unsolicited and made fascinating reading. I passed it on to the parties who should have been interested; as it turned out, they apparently weren't.

With growing maturity and a better understanding of what still remained to be done in the way of engineering development, we decided to concentrate on nearer objectives than the Moon and planets. By the late 1940s it was obvious that small satellite vehicles could be developed in the near future and would be of enormous scientific value.

In 1951, all these ideas came to a head when we arranged an international congress in London, on the theme of the artificial satellite. It was well attended by scientists from many countries, and one paper described the construction of a satellite vehicle of a size and performance very similar to the later Vanguard. This was designed to put into orbit an inflatable metallized balloon; less than ten years later, the whole world was to watch such an object – the moving star of Echo 1.

By this time (and, if I may say so, none too soon) official circles in the United States had started to take a mild interest in space. A few far-sighted individuals had already done much more, frequently to the annoyance of their superiors. (I once heard General Shriever remark that he still keeps, in his safe, a Department of Defense directive forbidding him to use the word 'space' in any public statements.)

Among the post-war American converts was a young physicist named Fred Singer, then a science attaché with the US Office of Naval Research. He had already done notable work with rocket probes in the upper atmosphere, but was somewhat sceptical about space flight. However, after a few brainwashing sessions he became wildly enthusiastic, and we soon had to hold him down lest he start galloping all over the Solar System.

One evening Fred, Val Cleaver and I were sitting in the Arts Theatre Club, thinking of ways to drum up interest in scientific satellites. 'What we want,' said someone, after the second or third round of drinks, 'is a nice snappy name for the project.' That started us doodling, and after a little while we concocted the abbreviation MOUSE for Minimum Orbital Unmanned Satellite of Earth. In the next few months, Fred produced a blizzard of papers describing what MOUSE (better still, MICE) could do; his predictions were uncannily accurate, and every one of them has since come true. The publicity campaign was extremely successful, and MOUSE appeared in technical journals all over the world. Indeed, a few years later an American news agency picked up one of Fred's drawings from a Russian paper and hawked it around as an example of a genuine Sputnik!

Our conversion of Fred Singer into a space cadet was probably one of the most important things we ever did. Quite apart from his missionary work in the more backward and savage areas of US science, he played a dominant role on the committee that recommended the launching of an International Geophysical Year (IGY) satellite. Though several other groups, and many individuals, were working towards the same end, Singer's intervention at a crucial moment, known only to a handful of people, was quite possibly decisive in committing the United States to a satellite programme. That it was the wrong satellite was not his fault.

On 29 July 1955 I was about as far from Washington as one could get, for I was living in a small wooden hut on an island of the Great Barrier Reef, thirty miles off the coast of Queensland. Coming in from a morning's diving along the reef, I happened to switch on the radio and was transfixed by the news that President Eisenhower had authorized the launching of scientific satellites during the International Geophysical Year. At great difficulty and expense I dispatched Singer a cable saying, 'Congratulations – may MOUSE bring forth a mountain.' When the message finally reached civilization by pearling lugger and aborigine postman, it was indecipherably distorted, and to add insult to injury the charges had got reversed in the process. It was a couple of years before I caught up with Fred and straightened things out.

Just as the V2, in 1945, marked the end of the first era of astronautics, so the announcement of Project Vanguard, ten years later, marked the end of the second. As far as we old space hands were concerned, the long campaign was over. A major power was now in the satellite business, reluctantly but inescapably. Given time, everything that we had predicted was bound to follow. Some of us hoped that we might live to see the first landing on the Moon – though in one of my early novels I had stuck my neck out by suggesting 1978 as a target date. Today, anyone so pessimistic would be extremely unpopular at NASA headquarters.

That our time scale might be a little inaccurate I began to suspect in the small hours of 4 October 1957, when a London paper roused me from my bed in a Barcelona hotel and asked if I cared to comment on a news flash just received from Moscow. There is no need to elaborate upon what has happened since then; it is enough to list some of the names that have now passed into history: Sputnik, Laika, Lunik, Gagarin, Shepard, Titov, Glenn, Mercury, Telstar, Mariner . . . these are merely the first words in the vast new vocabulary of space.

It has been a privilege to watch the beginnings, and to have taken some small part in the greatest adventure upon which the human race has ever embarked, but now it has grown too unimaginably huge for the comfort of amateurs like myself. This has struck me many times in the last few years – never so strongly as in the Grand Ballroom of the Waldorf Astoria, in the autumn of 1961.

There, some two thousand scientists and engineers, all in evening dress, had assembled for the banquet which concluded the American Rocket Society's Space Flight Report to the Nation. The cream of the astronautics industry (soon to be the largest business in the world) was gathered together; had the roof fallen in, that would have been the end of the United States' space effort and of its Vice-President Johnson, for he was the guest of honour, speaking on a nationwide hook-up.

Yes, it was an impressive occasion, and I was happy to be there. But I could not help thinking of the little pubs and tearooms where we met between the wars and dreamed the dreams we never thought to see come true.

The new generation will know the drama, the triumphs, the excitement, the responsibility of space flight.

But we had most of the fun.

— 2 —

Opening Frontiers

This chapter consists of extracts from the author's pioneering studies, Interplanetary Flight *(1950) and* The Exploration of Space *(1951), raising many issues which are amplified by later knowledge and events in subsequent chapters of this book. (JB)*

In his vain search for spices, Columbus certainly never dreamed of the far greater treasure that would one day gush from the oil wells of the New World; and the first men to survey the barren wastes of the Canadian Arctic – which to many must have seemed as unrewarding as the deserts of the Moon – could never have guessed of the faintly radioactive metal that lay guarding its secrets beneath their feet.

No one can ever foresee what role a new land may play in history; and we are considering now not merely new countries, or even continents – but worlds.

No investment pays better dividends to humanity than scientific research, though it sometimes has to wait a century or two for the profits. There is always an immense resistance to any change and a desire to preserve the status quo. Protagonists of space flight frequently used to meet the remark, 'Why go to the Moon? What's wrong with this Earth anyway?' Although the latter statement is seldom encountered these days, it has been succeeded by the query, 'Why not devote all this effort to developing our own world before going to others?'

Many of the indirect consequences of space travel will in fact help us to develop our own world – probably in ways at least as unforeseeable as those in which the American oilfields and farmlands assisted the development of Europe. It is not merely the physical sciences which will benefit: consider, for example, the possibilities of medical research opened up by 'free-fall' or low-gravity conditions. Who can say how much our lives are shortened by the heart's continual battle against gravity? On the Moon, sufferers from cardiac trouble might live normal lives – and normal lives might be greatly prolonged. This is only a random example of the way astronautics may conceivably affect mankind vitally and directly.

But the important consequences of space flight, and the main reasons for its accomplishment, are intangible, and to understand them we must look not to the future but the past. Although man has occupied the greater part of the habitable globe for thousands of years, until only five centuries ago he lived – psychologically – not in one world but in many. Each of the great cultures in the belt from Britain to Japan was insulated from its neighbours by geography or deliberate choice: each was convinced that it alone represented the flower of civilization, and that all else was barbarism.

The 'unification of the world', to use Toynbee's somewhat optimistic phrase, became possible only when the sailing ship and the arts of navigation were developed sufficiently to replace the difficult overland routes by the easier sea passages. The result was the great age of exploration whose physical climax was the discovery of the Americas, and whose supreme intellectual achievement was the liberation of the human spirit. Perhaps no better symbol of the questing mind of Renaissance man could be found than the lonely ship sailing steadfastly towards new horizons, until east and west had merged at last and the circumnavigation of the globe had been achieved.

The importance of exploration does not lie merely in the opportunities it gives to adolescent (but not to be despised) desires for excitement and variety. It is no mere accident that the age of Columbus was also the age of Leonardo, or that Sir Walter Raleigh was a contemporary of Shakespeare and Galileo. 'In human records,' wrote the anthropologist J. D. Unwin, 'there is no trace of any display of productive energy which has not been preceded by a display of expansive energy.' And today, all possibility of expansion on Earth itself has practically ceased.

The thought is a sombre one. Even if it survives the hazards of war, our culture is proceeding under a momentum which must be exhausted in the foreseeable future. Fabre once described how he linked the two ends of a chain of marching caterpillars so that they circled endlessly in a closed loop. Even if we avoid all other disasters, this would appear a fitting symbol of humanity's eventual fate when the impetus of the last few centuries has reached its peak and died away. For a closed culture, though it may endure for centuries, is inherently unstable. It may decay quietly and crumble into ruin, or it may be disrupted violently by internal conflicts. Space travel is a necessary, though not in itself a sufficient, way of escape from this predicament.

It is now four hundred years since Copernicus destroyed medieval cosmology and dethroned the Earth from the centre of creation. Shattering though the repercussions of that fall were in the fields of science and philosophy, they scarcely touched the ordinary man. To him this planet is still the whole of the Universe: he knows that other worlds exist, but the knowledge does not affect his life and therefore has little real meaning to him.

All this could be changed as the twentieth century draws to its end. Into a few decades may be compressed more profound alterations to our world picture than occurred during the whole of the Renaissance and the age of discovery that followed. To our children the Moon may become what the Americas were four hundred years ago – a world of unknown danger, promise and opportunity. No longer are Mars and Venus merely the names of wandering lights seldom glimpsed by the dwellers in cities. They will be more familiar than ever they were to those eastern watchers who first marked their movements, for they will be the new frontiers of the human mind.

These new frontiers are urgently needed. The crossing of space may do much to reduce the tensions of our age by turning men's minds outwards and away from their tribal conflicts. It may well be that only by acquiring this new sense of boundless frontiers will the world break free from the ancient cycle of war and peace. One wonders how even the most stubborn of nationalisms can survive when men have seen the Earth as a pale crescent dwindling against the stars, until at last they look for it in vain.

So there is a much more fundamental reply to that earlier question, 'Why not devote all this effort to developing our own world before going to others?', and one cannot help thinking that those who ask it have overlooked the facts of human nature. One wonders if they would have asked Phidias, when he was starting work on the Parthenon frieze, why he was not engaged on something useful like rebuilding the Athenian slums. If he had kept his temper, the artist would probably have answered that he was doing the only job that interested him. So it is, in the ultimate analysis, with those who want to cross space.

There are, it seems, some people who have definite psychological objections to space flight. In certain cases this has a religious basis – it is a new form of the old feeling that, in some mysterious way, there are things that 'man was never intended to do'. We do not know a better way of demolishing this superstition than by referring to the old lady who remarked that aeroplanes were undoubtedly an invention of the Devil, 'since men should travel in trains as God intended them to'.

Others, one suspects, are afraid that the crossing of space, and above all contact with intelligent but non-human races, may destroy the foundations of their religious faith. They may be right, but in any event their attitude is one which does not bear logical examination – for a faith which cannot survive collision with the truth is not worth many regrets.

The races of other worlds will have senses and philosophies very different from our own. To recall Plato's famous analogy, we are prisoners in a cave, gathering our impressions of the outside world from shadows thrown upon the walls. We may never escape to reach that outer reality, but one day we may hope to reach other prisoners in adjoining caves, where we may learn far more than we could ever do by our own unaided efforts.

Yet space travel will not, as some fear, destroy the mystery of the Universe. On the contrary, it may indeed increase it. Although many specific problems will be solved and many doubts settled, our area of contact with the unknown will be enormously magnified. This has always been the case with scientific research: it should never be forgotten that, despite all our knowledge, we live in a far more wonderful and even more mysterious world than did our ancestors. We will not exhaust the marvels of the physical Universe until we have explored the whole Cosmos – and *that* prospect is still, to say the least, satisfyingly remote, if indeed it is theoretically possible. We have scarcely begun a voyage of discovery which may never have an end.

Somewhere on that journey we may at last learn what purpose, if any, life plays in the Universe of matter: certainly we can never learn it on this Earth alone. Among the stars lies the proper study of mankind. Pope's aphorism gave only part of the truth: for the proper study of mankind is not merely Man, but Intelligence.

There will, it is true, be danger in space, as there has always been on the oceans or in the air. Some of these dangers we may guess: others we shall not know until we meet them. Nature is no friend of man's, and the most that he can hope for is her neutrality. But if he meets destruction, it will be at his own hands and according to a familiar pattern.

The dream of flight was one of the noblest, and one of the most disinterested, of all man's aspirations. Yet it led in the end to that silver Superfortress driving in passionless beauty through August skies towards the city whose name it was to sear into the conscience of the world. Already there has been half-serious talk concerning the use of the Moon for military bases and launching sites. The crossing of space may thus bring, not a new Renaissance, but the final catastrophe which haunts our generation.

That is the danger, the dark thundercloud that threatens the promise of the dawn. The rocket has already been the instrument of evil, and may be so again. But there is no way back into the past: the choice, as Wells once said, is the Universe – or nothing. Though men and civilizations may yearn for rest, for the dream of the lotus-eaters, that is a desire that merges imperceptibly into death. The challenge of the great spaces between the worlds is a stupendous one; but if we fail to meet it, the story of our race will be final and inevitable. Humanity will have turned its back upon the still untrodden heights and will be descending the long slope that stretches, across a thousand million years of time, down to the shores of the primeval sea.

One would give much to know what verdict a historian of the year 3000 – as detached from us as we are from the Crusaders – would pass upon our age, as he looks back at us down the long perspective of time. Let us hope that this will be his judgement:

The twentieth century was, without question, the most momentous hundred years in the history of mankind. It opened with the conquest of the air, and before it had run half its course had presented civilization with its supreme challenge – the control of atomic energy. Yet even these events, each of which changed the world, were soon to be eclipsed. To us a thousand years later, the whole story of mankind before the twentieth century seems like the prelude to some great drama, played on the narrow strip of stage before the curtain has risen and revealed the scenery. For countless generations of men, that tiny, crowded stage – the planet Earth – was the whole of creation, and they the only actors. Yet towards the close of that fabulous century, the curtain began slowly, inexorably to rise, and man realized at last that the Earth was only one of many worlds; the Sun only one among many stars. The coming of the rocket brought to an end a million years of isolation. With the landing of the first spaceship on Mars and Venus, the childhood of our race was over and history as we know it began . . .

— 3 —

The Challenge of the Spaceship

This was a revised version of a talk delivered to the British Interplanetary Society in 1946 during my first term as chairman. The essay in many ways marks the beginning of my literary career, being chosen by the distinguished critic Ivor Brown for a prestigious volume British Thought *(1947). I am still rather proud of the fact that when I sent the first printed version to George Bernard Shaw (see page 18) he promptly joined the British Interplanetary Society, and remained a member until his death.*

A historian of the twenty-first century, looking back past our own age to the beginnings of human civilization, will be conscious of four great turning points which mark the end of one era and the dawn of a new and totally different mode of life. Two of these events are lost, probably for ever, in the primeval night before history began. The invention of agriculture led to the founding of settled communities and gave man the leisure and social intercourse without which progress is impossible. The taming of fire made him virtually independent of climate and, most important of all, led to the working of metals and so set him upon the road of technological development – that road which was to lead, centuries later, to the steam engine, the Industrial Revolution, and the age of steel and gasoline and surface transportation through which we are now passing.

The third revolution began, as all the world knows, in a squash court in Chicago on 2 December 1942, when the first self-sustaining nuclear reaction was started by man. We are still too close to that cataclysmic event to see it in its true perspective, but we know that it will change our world, for better or for worse, almost beyond recognition. And we know too that it is linked with the fourth and in some ways greatest change of all – the crossing of space and the exploration of the other planets. For though the first space vehicles were chemically fuelled, only atomic energy is adequate to lift really large payloads out of the Earth's gravitational field – that invisible maelstrom whose tug can still be felt a million miles away.

Prophecy is a dangerous and thankless business, frequently fatal to those who practise it. We have, however, learned from past experience that even the most extravagant forecast seldom overtakes the truth. H. G. Wells once wrote – and was no doubt laughed to scorn for his folly – that the airplane might have some influence upon warfare by the year 1950. He never dared to imagine that by that date aircraft would not only have become of supreme importance but would have been challenged by still newer weapons.

It is certainly not being rash – it may indeed be conservative – to assume that by the last quarter of this century an efficient and reliable method of nuclear propulsion for space vehicles will have been perfected. Atomic power is hardly likely to advance the conquest of space by more than ten years, but it may make it practical almost from the beginning. It would mean that the whole Solar System, and not merely the Moon, would be immediately accessible to man. As our first space probes have demonstrated, it requires very little more power to reach the planets than it does to go to the Moon, but the most economical voyages involve months or even years of free coasting along orbits curving half-way round the sun. With atomic power these journeys could be cut to a fraction of the time. For example, the 'cheapest' journey to Mars – as far as fuel is concerned – lasts 258 days. With a nuclear-propelled ship, travelling by a more direct route at quite a moderate speed, it need take only a few weeks.

There are still some scientists who consider that there is no point in sending men into space, even when it becomes technically possible; machines, they argue, can do all that is necessary. Such an outlook is incredibly short-sighted; worse than that, it is stupid, for it completely ignores human nature. Though the specific ideals of astronautics are new, the motives and impulses underlying them are as old as the race – and, in the ultimate analysis, they owe as much to emotion as to reason. Even if we could learn nothing in space that our instruments would not already tell us, we should go there just the same.

Some men compose music or spend their lives trying to catch and hold for ever the last colours of the dying day, or a pattern of clouds that, through all eternity, will never come again. Others make voyages of exploration across the world, while some make equally momentous journeys in quiet studies with no more equipment than pencil and paper. If you asked these men the purpose of their music, their painting, their exploring or their mathematics, they would probably say that they hoped to increase the beauty or the knowledge in the world. That answer would be true, and yet misleading. Very few indeed would give the simpler, more fundamental reason that they had no choice in the matter – that what they did, they did because they had to.

The urge to explore, to discover, to 'follow knowledge like a sinking star', is a primary human impulse which needs, and can receive, no further justification than its own existence. The search for knowledge, said a modern Chinese philosopher, is a form of play. If this be true, then the spaceship, when it comes, will be the ultimate toy that may lead mankind from its cloistered nursery out into the playground of the stars.

However, it is not hard to think of endless and entirely valid 'practical' reasons why one should wish to cross space, and some of these we will discuss later. There is no doubt that eventually sheer necessity would bring about the conquest of the other planets. It may well be impossible to have a virile, steadily advancing culture limited to a single world, and taking the long-term – the very long-term – view, we know that our Earth will one day become uninhabitable. The Sun is still evolving, growing steadily hotter as its central fires become banked up beneath their accumulated 'ash' of helium. In the far future the oceans will boil back into the skies from which they once condensed, and life must pass from the planet Earth.

But the human race will not wait until it is kicked out. Long before the Sun's radiation has shown any measurable increase, man will have explored all the Solar System and, like a cautious bather testing the temperature of the sea, will be making breathless little forays into the abyss that separates him from the stars.

The last quarter of this century has been an age of exploration such as man has never before known. By the year 2000, most of the major bodies in the Solar System will probably have been reached, but it will take centuries to examine them all in any detail. Those who seem to think that the Moon is the goal of interplanetary travel should remember that the Solar System contains eight other planets, at least thirty moons and some thousands of asteroids. The total area of the major bodies is about two hundred and fifty times that of Earth, though the four giant planets probably do not possess stable surfaces on which landings could be made. Nevertheless, that still leaves an area ten times as great as all the continents of Earth.

This, then, is the future which lies before us, if our civilization survives the diseases of its childhood. It is a future which some may find terrifying, as no doubt our ancestors found the hostile emptiness of the great oceans. But the men who built our world crossed those oceans and overcame those fears. If we fail before the same test, our race will have begun its slide into decadence. Remember, too, that when the great explorers of the past set sail into the unknown they said goodbye for years to their homes and everything they knew. Our children will face no such loneliness. When they are among the outermost planets, when Earth is lost in the glare of the Sun and the Sun itself is no more than the brightest of the stars, they will still be able to hear its voice and to send their own words in a few hours back to the world of men.

Let us now consider the effects which interplanetary travel must have upon human institutions and ideas. The most obvious and direct result of the crossing of space will be a revolution in almost all branches of science. I will not attempt to list more than a few of the discoveries we may make when we can set up research stations and observatories upon the other planets, or in satellite orbits. One can never predict the outcome of any scientific investigation, and the greatest discoveries of all – the ones which will most influence human life – may come from sciences as yet unborn.

Astronomy and physics will, of course, be the fields of knowledge most immediately affected. In both these sciences there are whole areas where research has come to a dead end, or has never been started, because our terrestrial environment makes it impossible.

The atmosphere, which on a clear night looks so transparent, is in reality a coloured filter blocking all rays beyond the ultraviolet. Even in the visible spectrum the light that finally struggles through the shifting strata above our heads is so distorted that the images it carries dance and tremble in the field of the telescope.

An observatory on the Moon, working with quite small instruments, would be many times as effective as one on Earth. Far greater magnifications could be employed, and far longer exposures used. In addition, the low gravity would make relatively simple the building of larger telescopes than have ever been constructed on this planet.

In physics and chemistry, access to vacuums of unlimited extent will open up quite new fields of investigation. The electronic scientist may well look forward to the day when he can build radio tubes miles long, if he wishes, merely by setting up his electrodes in the open! It is also interesting to speculate whether we may not learn more about gravity when we can escape partially or wholly from its influence.

Artificial satellites have already given dramatic notice of what may be achieved when we can establish permanent, manned stations in space for observation and research. Accurate weather forecasting – which, it has been estimated, would be worth five billion dollars a year to the United States alone – will probably be impossible until we can hoist the meteorologists out into space, however reluctant they may be to go there. Only from a height of several thousand miles is it possible to observe the Earth's weather pattern as a whole, and to see literally at a glance the movement of storms and rain areas.

One application of space stations and satellites, whose importance it is impossible to overestimate, is their use for communications and TV relaying. Many years ago (in the British radio magazine *Wireless World*, October 1945) I pointed out that satellite-home transmitters could provide interference-free reception over the whole Earth, and might indeed be the only means of establishing a global TV service. To the best of my knowledge, this was the first appearance of this now commonplace idea. I have since wondered, a little wistfully, if I could have patented it.

Should any one nation establish a satellite relay chain, it would do more than dominate the world's communications. The cultural and political impact of TV news and entertainment broadcast directly to every home on Earth would be immeasurable. When one considers the effect of TV upon ostensibly educated populations, the impact upon the semi-literate peoples of Africa and Asia may be decisive. It may well determine whether English or Russian becomes the leading world language by the end of this century.

Yet these first direct results of astronautics may be less important, in the long run, than its indirect consequences. This has proved true in the past of most great scientific achievements. Copernican astronomy, Darwin's theory of evolution, Freudian psychology – these had few immediate practical results, but their effect on human thought was tremendous.

We may expect the same of astronautics. With the expansion of the world's mental horizons may come one of the greatest outbursts of creative activity ever known. The parallel with the Renaissance, with its great flowering of the arts and sciences, is very suggestive. 'In human records,' wrote the anthropologist J. D. Unwin, 'there is no trace of any display of productive energy which has not been preceded by a display of expansive energy. Although the two kinds of energy must be carefully distinguished, in the past they have been . . . united in the sense that one has developed out of the other.' Unwin continues with this quotation from Sir James Frazer: 'Intellectual progress, which reveals itself in the growth of art and science . . . receives an immense impetus from conquest and empire.' Interplanetary travel is now the only form of 'conquest and empire' compatible with civilization. Without it, the human mind, compelled to circle for ever in its planetary goldfish bowl, must eventually stagnate.

We all know the narrow, limited type of mind which is interested in nothing beyond its town or village, and bases its judgements on those parochial standards. We are slowly – perhaps too slowly – evolving from that mentality towards a world outlook. Few things will do more to accelerate that evolution than the conquest of space. It is not easy to see how the more extreme forms of nationalism can long survive when men begin to see the Earth in its true perspective as a single small globe among the stars.

There is, of course, the possibility that as soon as space is crossed all the great powers will join in a race to claim as much territory as their ships can reach. Some American writers have even suggested that for its own protection the United States must occupy the Moon to prevent its being used as a launching site for atomic rockets. Fantastic though such remarks may seem today, they represent a danger which it would be unwise to ignore. The menace of interplanetary imperialism can be overcome only by world-wide technical and political agreements well in advance of the actual event, and these will require continual pressure and guidance from the organizations which have studied the subject.

The Solar System is rather a large place, though whether it will be large enough for so quarrelsome an animal as *Homo sapiens* remains to be seen. But it is surely reasonable to hope that the crossing of space will have a considerable effect in reducing the psychological pressures and tensions of our present world. Much depends, of course, on the habitability of the other planets. It is not likely that very large populations will, at least for many centuries, be able to subsist outside the Earth. There may be no worlds in the Solar System upon which men can live without mechanical aids, and some of the greatest achievements of future engineering will be concerned with shaping hostile environments to human needs.

We must not, however, commit the only too common mistake of equating mere physical expansion, or even increasing scientific knowledge, with 'progress' – however that may be defined. Only little minds are impressed by sheer size and number. There would be no virtue in possessing the Universe if it brought neither wisdom nor happiness. Yet possess it we must, at least in spirit, if we are ever to answer the questions that men have asked in vain since history began.

Perhaps analogy will make my meaning clearer. Picture a small island inhabited by a race which has not yet learned the art of making ships. Looking out across the ocean this people can see many other islands, some of them much the same as its own but most of them clearly very different. From some of these islands, it is rumoured, the smoke of fires has been seen ascending – though whether those fires are the work of men, no one can say.

Now these islanders are very thoughtful people, and writers of many books with such resounding titles as *The Nature of the Universe*, *The Meaning of Life*, *Mind and Reality* and so on. Whilst admiring their enterprise, I do not think we should take their conclusions very seriously – at least until they have gone a little further afield than their own coral reef. As Robert Bridges wrote in 'The Testament of Beauty': 'Wisdom will repudiate thee, if thou think to enquire WHY things are as they are or whence they came: thy task is first to learn WHAT IS . . . '

That task the human race can scarcely begin to undertake while it is still Earthbound.

Every thoughtful man has often asked himself, Is our race the only intelligence in the Universe, or are there other, perhaps far higher, forms of life elsewhere? There can be few questions more important than this, for upon its outcome may depend all philosophy – yes, and all religion too.

The first discovery of planets revolving round other suns, which was made in the United States in 1942,* has changed all ideas of the plurality of worlds. Planets are far commoner than we had ever believed: there may be thousands of millions in this Galaxy alone. Few men today would care to argue that the Earth must be the only abode of life in the whole of space.

It is true – it is even likely – that we may encounter no other intelligence in the Solar System. That contact may have to wait for the day, perhaps ages hence, when we can reach the stars. But sooner or later it must come.

There have been many portrayals in literature of these fateful meetings. Most science-fiction writers, with characteristic lack of imagination, have used them as an excuse for stories of conflict and violence indistinguishable from those which stain the pages of our own history. Such an attitude shows a complete misunderstanding of the factors involved.

Remember the penny and the postage stamp which Sir James Jeans, in *The Mysterious Universe*, balanced on Cleopatra's Needle. The obelisk represented the age of the world, the penny the whole duration of man's existence, and the stamp the length of time in which he has been slightly civilized. The period during which life will be possible on Earth corresponds to a further column of stamps hundreds of yards – perhaps a mile – in height.

Thinking of this picture, we see how infinitely improbable it is that the question of interplanetary warfare can ever arise. Any races

---

*But later found to be erroneous!

we encounter will almost certainly be superhuman or subhuman – more likely the former, since ours must surely be one of the youngest cultures in the Universe. Only if we score a bull's-eye on that one stamp in the mile-high column will we meet a race at a level of technical development sufficiently near our own for warfare to be possible. If ships from Earth ever set out to conquer other worlds they may find painted war canoes drawing slowly into New York Harbour.

But if the Universe does hold species so greatly in advance of our own, then why have they never visited Earth? There is one very simple answer to this question. Let us suppose that such races exist: let us even suppose that, never having heard of Einstein, they can pass from one end of the Galaxy to the other as quickly as they wish. That will help them less than one might think. In ten minutes, a man may walk along a beach – but in his whole lifetime he could not examine every grain of sand upon it. For all that we know, there may be fleets of survey ships diligently charting and recharting the Universe. Even making the most optimistic assumptions, they could scarcely have visited our world in the few thousand years of recorded history.

Perhaps, even at this moment, there lies in some rather extensive filing system a complete report on this planet, with maps which to us would look distorted but still recognizable. That report would show that though Earth was teeming with life, it had no dominant species. However, certain social insects showed considerable promise, and the file might end with the note, 'Intelligence may be emerging on this planet. Suggest that intervals between surveys be reduced to a million years.'

Very well, you may ask; suppose we encounter beings who judge, condemn and execute us as dispassionately, and with as little effort, as we spray a pool of mosquito larvae with DDT? I must admit that the possibility exists, and the logical answer – that their reasons will no doubt be excellent – is somewhat lacking in appeal. However, this prospect seems remote. I do not believe that any culture can advance, for more than a few centuries at a time, on a technological front alone. Morals and ethics must not lag behind science, otherwise the social system will breed poisons which will cause its certain destruction. I believe therefore that with superhuman knowledge must go equally great compassion and tolerance. In this I may be utterly wrong: the future may yet belong to forces which we should call cruel and evil. Whatever we may hope, we cannot be certain that human aspirations and ideals have universal validity. This we can discover in one way only, and the philosophical mind will be willing to pay the price of knowledge.

I have mentioned before how limited our picture of the Universe must be so long as we are confined to this Earth alone. But the story does not end there. Our impressions of reality are determined, perhaps more than we imagine, by the senses through which we make contact with the external world. How utterly different our cosmologies would have been had Nature economized with us, as she has done with other creatures, and given us eyes incapable of seeing the stars! Yet how pitiably limited are the eyes we do possess, tuned as they are to a single octave in an endless spectrum! The world in which we live is drenched with invisible radiations, from the microwaves which we have just discovered coming from Sun and stars, to the cosmic rays whose origin is still one of the prime mysteries of modern physics. These things we have discovered within the last generation, and we cannot guess what still lies beneath the threshold of the senses – though recent discoveries in paranormal psychology hint that the search may be only beginning.

The races of other worlds will have senses and philosophies very different from our own. To recall Plato's famous analogy, we are prisoners in a cave, gathering our impressions of the outside world from shadows thrown upon the walls. We may never escape to reach that outer reality, but one day we may hope to meet other prisoners in adjoining caves, where the shadows may be very different and where we may learn far more than we could ever do by our own unaided efforts.

These are deep waters, and it is time to turn back to the shore, to leave the distant dream for the present reality of fuels and motors, of combustion-chamber pressures and servomechanisms. Yet I make no apology for discussing these remote vistas at some length, if only to show the triviality of the viewpoint which regards interplanetary travel as a schoolboy adventure of no more real value than the scaling of some hitherto inaccessible mountain. The adventure is there, it is true, and that is good in itself – but it is only a small part of a much greater whole.

Not so short-sighted, but equally false, is the view expressed by Professor C. S. Lewis, who has written of would-be astronauts in this unflattering fashion: 'The destruction or enslavement of other species in the universe, if such there are, is to these minds a welcome corollary.' In case there are any to whom this prospect still appeals, I would point out that empires, like atomic bombs, are self-liquidating assets. Dominance by force leads to revolution, which in the long run, even if indirectly, must be successful. Humane government leads eventually to self-determination and equality, as the classic case of the British Empire has shown. Commonwealths alone can be stable and enduring, but empires must always contain the seeds of their own dissolution.

The desire to give a comprehensive picture of the outcome of astronautics has compelled me to range – not unwillingly – over an enormous field. However, I do not wish anyone to think that the possibilities we have been discussing need come in this century, or the next, or the next. Yet any of them may arise, at any time, as soon as the first ships begin to leave the Earth. Man's first contact with other intelligent races may lie as far away in time as the building of the pyramids – or it may be as near as the discovery of X-rays.

Of this, at least, we may be fairly certain. Barring accidents – the most obvious of which I need not specify – the exploration of the planets will be in full swing as this century draws to its close. To examine them in any detail, and to exploit their possibilities fully, will take hundreds of years. But man being what he is, when his first ship circles down into the frozen wastes of Pluto, his mind will already be bridging the gulf still lying between him and the stars.

Interplanetary distances are a million times as great as those to which we are accustomed in everyday life, but interstellar distances are a millionfold greater still. Before them even light is a hopeless laggard, taking years to pass from one star to its neighbour. How man will face this stupendous challenge I do not know; but face it one day he will. Professor J. D. Bernal was, I believe, the first to suggest that one solution might lie in the use of artificial planets, little self-contained worlds embarking upon journeys which would last for generations. Olaf Stapledon has expanded this theme in *Star*

Maker, one of the greatest of his fantasies, but the thought of these tiny bubbles of life, creeping from star to star on their age-long journeys, carrying whole populations doomed never to set foot upon any planet, never to know the passage of the seasons or even the interchange of night and day, is one from which we might well recoil in horror. However, those who would make such journeys would have outlooks very different from our own and we cannot judge their minds by our standards.

These speculations, intriguing though they are, will hardly concern mankind in this century. We may, I think, confidently expect that it will be a hundred years at least before confinement to the Solar System produces very marked signs of claustrophobia.

Our survey is now finished. We have gone as far as is possible, at this moment of time, in trying to assess the impact of astronautics upon human affairs. I am not unmindful of the fact that fifty years from now, instead of preparing for the conquest of the outer planets, our grandchildren may be dispossessed savages clinging to the fertile oases in a radioactive wilderness. Yet we must keep the problems of today in their true proportions. They are of vital – indeed of supreme – importance, since they can destroy our civilization and slay the future before its birth. But if we survive them, they will pass into history and the time will come when they will be as little remembered as the causes of the Punic Wars. The crossing of space – even the sense of its imminent achievement in the years before it comes – may do much to turn men's minds outward and away from their present tribal squabbles. In this sense the rocket, far from being one of the destroyers of civilization, may provide the safety valve that is needed to preserve it.

This point may be of the utmost importance. By providing an outlet for man's exuberant and adolescent energies, astronautics may make a truly vital contribution to the problems of the present world. In many ways, the very dynamic qualities of astronautics are in tune with the restless, expansive spirit of our age.

In this essay I have tried to show that the future development of mankind, on the spiritual no less than the material plane, is bound up with the conquest of space. To what may be called – using the words in the widest possible sense – the liberal scientific mind, I believe these arguments to be unanswerable. The only real criticism that may be raised against them is the quantitative one that the world is not yet ready for such changes. It is hard not to sympathize with this view, which may be correct, but I have given my reasons for thinking otherwise.

The future of which I have spoken is now being shaped by men working with slide rules in quiet offices, and by men taking instrument readings amid the savage roar of harnessed jets. Some are engineers, some are dreamers – but many are both. The time will come when they can say with T. E. Lawrence, 'All men dream; but not equally. Those who dream by night in the dusty recesses of their minds wake in the day to find that it was vanity: but the dreamers of the day are dangerous men, for they may act their dream with open eyes, to make it possible.'

Thus it has always been in the past, for our civilization is no more than the sum of all the dreams that earlier ages have brought to fulfilment. And so it must always be, for if men cease to dream, if they turn their backs upon the wonder of the Universe, the story of our race will be coming to an end.

Space Flight – Imagination and Reality

Lecture at the Second United Nations Conference on the Exploration and Peaceful Uses of Outer Space (UNISPACE '82), Vienna, 10 August 1982.

The exploration of space was anticipated for centuries before the reality met the dream. It is not only interesting but also valuable to look back on some of those old ideas and speculations, to see what we can learn from their successes as well as their failures. For much that has occurred since the Space Age opened in 1957 was foreseen with remarkable accuracy; yet there were also some stunning surprises. So it will be in the future.

It is somewhat ironic that the first truly *scientific* space voyage involved supernatural forces. This was the *Somnium* (1643) written by no less a man than Kepler – to whom astronautics owes as much as to Newton himself. The discoverer of the laws governing the motion of planets – and hence of spaceships – was both a scientist and a mystic; his background may be judged by the fact that his own mother barely escaped execution for sorcery.

In the *Somnium*, Kepler employed demons to carry his hero to the Moon, and made the significant remark that as the voyage progressed it would no longer be necessary to use any force for propulsion. His description of the Moon, based on the knowledge revealed by the newly invented telescope, was also as scientifically accurate as was possible at the time – though, like many later writers, he assumed the existence of water, air, and life.

As is well known, demons are often unreliable servants, though perhaps not as unreliable as some of the early rockets. Other writers have used mysterious mental forces to carry their heroes to other worlds – often at speeds far exceeding the miserable velocity of light. Olaf Stapledon used such a device in his magnificent *Star*

Maker (1937), as did C. S. Lewis in *Perelandra* (1944; also known as *Voyage to Venus*). Descending slightly in the literary scale, Edgar Rice Burroughs used the power of the mind to transport his muscular hero, John Carter, to the planet Mars – or Barsoom, as its inhabitants call it. His example had a great influence on Carl Sagan, who has written, 'I can remember spending many an hour in my boyhood, arms resolutely outstretched in an empty field, imploring what I believed to be Mars to transport me there. It never worked.' From what we now know of conditions on Mars, it was very lucky for Carl that it didn't . . .

Some early writers who did not approve of trafficking with supernatural powers – transactions in which, however carefully one read the contract, there always seemed to be some un-suspected penalty clause – used natural agencies to convey their heroes away from Earth. This was the case with the ancestor of all space-travel stories, the *Vera Historia* (True History) written by Lucian of Samos in AD 160. In this misleadingly entitled tale, a ship sailing in the dangerous and unexplored region beyond the Pillars of Hercules was caught up in a whirlwind and deposited on the Moon. It is true that the Bay of Biscay has a bad reputation, but this must have been an unusually rough passage.

About a millennium and a half later, the great Jules Verne improved on this slightly with his *Hector Servadac* (1877), an unlikely tale in which a comet grazes the Earth, scoops up two Frenchmen, and takes them on a trip around the Solar System. As they explore the comet they encounter bits of the Earth that it had acquired during the collision – some of them still inhabited. A fragment of the Rock of Gibraltar is discovered, occupied by two Englishmen playing chess and, according to Verne, quite unaware of their predicament. I doubt this: it seems much more likely that they were perfectly aware of the fact that they were aboard a comet, but had come to a crucial point in their game and, with typically English sang-froid, refused to be distracted by such trivialities.

Perhaps the most ingenious use of natural forces was that employed by Cyrano de Bergerac in his classic *Voyages to the Moon and Sun* (1656). In the first of his several interplanetary voyages, the motive power was provided by vials of dew strapped round his waist – for Cyrano very logically argued that as the Sun sucked up the dew in the morning, it would carry him with it . . .

So much for magic; now for machines.

With the development of the scientific method in the seventeenth and eighteenth centuries, and a fuller understanding of what space travel *really* implied, authors went to greater lengths to give their stories some basis of plausibility, and the first primitive spaceships began to appear in literature. The discovery of explosives and the invention of artillery showed that there was one way of escaping from the Earth; and the 'spacegun' arrived on the scene.

The most famous version, of course, is that in Jules Verne's *From the Earth to the Moon* (1865), but it was not the first. That dubious honour goes to an obscure Irish writer, Murtagh McDermot, who as early as 1728 wrote *A Trip to the Moon*. Amazingly, he used a spacegun *to come home*, after persuading the Selenites to dig a great hole containing 7,000 barrels of gunpowder. He placed himself in the middle of ten concentric wooden vessels, 'to lessen the shock', and provided himself with wings so that he could glide down to Earth when he arrived.

How did he get to the Moon in the first place? By rocket! Altogether a remarkable effort for two and a half centuries ago. McDermot was certainly much more far-sighted than many of his successors.

Nearer our own time, it is difficult to say how seriously Verne took his mammoth cannon, because so much of the story is facetiously written, usually at the expense of the Americans. But he went to a great deal of trouble with his astronomical facts and figures; the 'Columbiad' was a 1,000-foot vertical barrel sunk in the Florida soil – not far from Cape Canaveral! – and packed with 200 tons of gun-cotton. The projectile itself was made of the newly discovered wonder-metal, aluminium.

Ignoring the slight impossibility of the passengers – or indeed the vehicle – surviving the concussion, Verne's projectile must be considered as the first scientifically conceived spacecraft. It had shock-absorbers, air-conditioning, padded walls with windows set in them and similar arrangements which we now accept as commonplace in any well-ordered spaceship.

The last – I hope – spacegun was that devised by H. G. Wells for his film *Things to Come* (1936). It was visually spectacular, but of course scientific nonsense, and we were quite upset. We wrote Mr Wells a 'more in sorrow than in anger' letter, and received a kind but unrepentant answer.

Because guns are so obviously impractical, there have been many attempts to devise alternative, and less violent, means of escaping from the Earth. The American writer Edward E. Hale, author of *The Brick Moon* (1870) – the very first suggestion ever made for an artificial satellite – proposed giant flywheels that could be brought up to speed over a long period of time. At the appropriate moment, the payload would be dropped on the rim and flicked into orbit. I need hardly say that *this* suggestion is even more absurd than a spacegun – as Hale undoubtedly knew, since he was writing with his tongue firmly in his cheek.

If you could make a gun long enough, of course, the initial shock might be reduced to acceptable figures; hence the concept of the launching track. The earliest version of this I have been able to discover is in a story called *The Moon Conquerors* (1930) by a German author, R. H. Romans. In this, a series of giant magnets was used to shoot a spaceship to the Moon, and many later authors have developed the same idea.

But the Earth-based launching track has some fundamental flaws. It would have to be at least six hundred miles long if human passengers were to survive the acceleration, so the cost would be astronomical. It could only do part of the job, though admittedly the most difficult part – the escape from Earth. The spacecraft would still require a self-contained propulsion system, for the landing and return. And as a last fatal defect – any object given the escape velocity of 6.9 miles a second near the surface of the Earth would burn up like a meteor in the dense lower atmosphere.

The only way an Earth-based launcher could operate is if it were built in the form of a slowly ascending ramp, the whole width of equatorial Africa or South America, starting from sea level and climbing to a height of, say, twelve miles. I do not know if anyone has ever had the temerity to suggest this, so I cheerfully do so now.

More than thirty years ago ('Electromagnetic Launching as a Major Contribution to Space-Flight', *JBIS* vol. 9, no. 6, November

1950) I pointed out that the ideal place for a launcher is the Moon – the low gravity, and absence of atmosphere, makes it the perfect location. Such a launcher could be used for countless purposes, since it could economically project material – and even fragile human passengers – to almost any point in the Solar System. This concept, re-christened the 'mass launcher', is the basis of the schemes for space-colonization recently popularized by Dr Gerard O'Neill (*The Higher Frontier*, 1976).

But you can't build a lunar launcher until you've escaped from the Earth, so it's no use in the pioneering days. Before the possibilities of the rocket were realized, many writers of space-travel stories sought an answer in forces that could overcome gravity. The most famous development of this idea is in H. G. Wells' *The First Men in the Moon* (1901) – still the greatest of all interplanetary stories, despite its inevitable dating.

Wells' 'Cavorite' was a substance which blocked gravity, just as a sheet of metal blocks light. You had only to coat a sphere with it, and you would fly away from the Earth. You could steer simply by removing the section of Cavorite facing the body you wished to approach, so that its attraction could act upon you. So much more civilized than those noisy and dangerous rockets!

Is such a thing even theoretically possible? As far as Cavorite is concerned, the answer is a resounding 'No', as can be very easily proved by a simple 'thought experiment'. Imagine a large flywheel, mounted vertically, with a sheet of Cavorite placed beneath one side. By definition, that side would be weightless, while the other half would have normal weight. Thus there would be a continual unbalance, so the wheel would revolve more and more rapidly. It could be a permanent source of energy – a perpetual motion machine, defying the most fundamental law of physics. QED.

Amusingly enough, Jules Verne pointed this out to the young Mr Wells in no uncertain terms. 'I make use of physics. He invents. I go to the Moon in a cannon-ball . . . he constructs a metal which does away with the law of gravitation . . . *très joli* – but show me this metal. Let him produce it.' Perhaps this justified criticism induced Wells, a third of a century later, to take his retrograde step of using the spacegun in *Things to Come*; but I rather doubt it. Wells was too great an artist to let himself be unduly restricted by mere facts.

Though a *passive* gravity shield of the type imagined by Wells (and many other writers, before and since) is impossible, the laws of physics do not rule out some interesting alternatives. There is no fundamental objection to a substance which is repelled, instead of being attracted, by gravity, just as similar electric charges repel each other. We are hardly likely to discover such a material on Earth, since if it ever occurred naturally it would long ago have shot off into space. But if we could manufacture such an interesting substance, then in principle it could be used to lift a spaceship – though we would have to jettison it to come home, or to land on another planet. The technique of travel with a gravity-repellent material would be rather like old-style hydrogen ballooning. The gas can take you up – but you have to get rid of it when you want to come down again.

Nor is there any objection to an anti-gravity device *which is driven by some appropriate source of energy*, so that it does not produce something for nothing. I suppose the innumerable 'space drives' of science fiction, some of which I have occasionally used myself, come under this heading. They may not defy the law of the conservation of energy, but it is hard to see how they can avoid a conflict with something equally fundamental – Newton's Third Law, that for every action there is an equal and opposite reaction. All motion, without exception, depends upon this Law. Even a spaceship must have something to push against; in the case of a rocket, of course, that something is its ejected propellant mass.

During the mid-1950s – just after the announcement of the Vanguard Earth Satellite Program, which may or may not have been a coincidence – there was a rash of reports from the United States about 'electro-gravitics'. The Princeton Institute for Advanced Studies, Convair, the Glen Martin Company, amongst others, were involved; Martin actually placed advertisements to recruit scientists 'interested in gravity'. The whole thing rapidly fizzled out; one cynic told me that it was 'much ado about nothing, started by a bunch of engineers who didn't know enough physics'. That certainly seems to have been the case. Electro-gravitics, like Exobiology, remains a science without a single specimen for study . . .

And yet – the subject is not closed, and probably never will be. A

few years ago one of the United Kingdom's best-known engineers –
Eric Laithwaite, Professor of Heavy Electrical Engineering at
Imperial College, London – startled everyone by claiming that a
system of two spinning gyroscopes could produce an out-of-balance
force; in other words, mechanically produced anti-gravity.

Interestingly enough, exactly the same conclusion was once
reached by *each of the great pioneers of astronautics* – Tsiolkovski,
Goddard, Oberth. As very young men, they all thought that some
arrangement of spinning weights could produce a lift, but very
quickly discovered a fallacy in their reasoning. Oberth has com-
plained that some inventor approaches him once a month, on the
average, with variants of this idea . . . But Professor Laithwaite is
no crackpot inventor, and proposes to conduct a crucial experiment on *his* system in the weightless environment of the Space
Shuttle. I wish him luck.

If we ever do invent a 'space drive', however, it will surely
depend upon some new fundamental discovery in sub-atomic
physics, or the structure of space-time. Until then, we are stuck
with rockets – chemical, electric or nuclear.

There is, it is true, one other known alternative, but that is of
very limited application. I refer to 'solar sailing'.

The fact that sunlight produces a tiny – but measurable – pressure when it falls upon a surface has already been used to control
the orientation of satellites. Since even a minute force can produce
large effects if it operates over a sufficiently long time, small
reflecting panels can be used to make a satellite turn round its axis
and point in any desired direction. If these panels were large
enough – and by large, I mean miles along a side – they could
produce major orbital changes.

Hence the delightful fantasy – and perhaps one day it may be
more than that – of 'solar yachts' unfurling gigantic, gossamer-
thin sails as they race from world to world. 'Solar sailing' would be
the most spectacular sport ever developed; but it will not be a very
exciting one, because even the simplest manoeuvre would take
hours or days. And as it is a technology which can only be used in
the zero-gravity vacuum of deep space, the use of the sun's radiation pressure for propulsion still depends on the rocket for its
initial stages.

Though it was mentioned in passing from time to time – for example by the ingenious Cyrano de Bergerac – the rocket did not enter the literature of space travel until surprisingly late. Its first serious appearance may have been in Verne's sequel *Round the Moon* (1870), where it was used to change the orbit of the projectile. Verne – unlike the *New York Times*, in a notorious editorial about Goddard's folly, half a century later – clearly understood that rockets could provide thrust in a vacuum. It is a pity he did not consider them adequate for the whole job; his impossible gun may have set back the conquest of space by years, though hardly by decades.

Popular attention began to be focused on rockets from 1925 onwards, with the appearance of serious technical literature and the rise of small experimental groups in Germany, the USSR and elsewhere. For a long time, fact and fiction were inextricably entangled; many of the pioneers were writers, and used their pens to spread the news that space travel need no longer be fantasy. It is hard to believe that this pioneering era is only half a century ago, and that a mere forty years after the flight of the first liquid-fuelled rocket in 1926, men were preparing to go to the Moon.

The 'Spaceflight Revolution', as William Sims Bainbridge called it in his book of that name, was one of the swiftest and most remarkable in human history. Most technological developments arise naturally when some social need is matched by a corresponding invention; the steam engine, the telephone, the automobile are obvious examples. But, to be perfectly honest, no one really *needed* spaceships in the mid-twentieth century, and a lot of people still rather wish they'd go away. Sooner or later, of course, space transportation would have evolved, probably out of high-altitude aviation, but things didn't happen that way. As Bainbridge points out, the imagination and determination of a mere handful of men – of whom the Russian Korolev and the German von Braun were by far the most important – opened up the space frontier decades ahead of any historically plausible scenario.

The full implications of this will not be known for centuries – but let me leave this analogy for you to meditate upon. In 1492 Christopher Columbus did something much more important than merely discovering America, which after all had been known to quite a few people for at least twenty thousand years. He opened up the road between the Old World and the New. Yet some Renaissance Korolev or von Braun *could* have made that happen fifty – a hundred – years earlier than it actually did; the Vikings almost succeeded. One day we may be very glad that we got to the Moon in 1969, instead of, well, 2001 . . . or even 2051 . . .

And to those who think that the landing on the Moon was merely a technological *tour de force* of little ultimate importance in human affairs, I offer another lesson from history. One of the early explorers of Australia reported proudly to his Mission Control, back in Whitehall, 'I have now mapped this continent so thoroughly *that no one need ever go there again.*' You may laugh – but as far as space is concerned, there are equally short-sighted people around today.

Among them I would include all those distinguished scientists who keep telling us that the exploration of space can best be carried out by robots. Well, Europe could have waited five hundred years and sent remote-controlled cameras to survey America. Of course, this is a ridiculous analogy – but then the whole debate is ridiculous. Robots are essential as pioneers and there are environments which only they can penetrate. But there are also missions where it is far more effective – and even cheaper – to have men in the loop, if only to deal with unexpected emergencies. (Remember the Skylab salvage operation, and Apollo 13?)

However, cost-effectiveness is not the only criterion. Like all his fellow-primates, man is an inquisitive animal, and seldom stops to calculate the numbers of bits per buck. He wants to go and see things for himself. And what he has discovered he never abandons, except temporarily – as in the case of the South Pole between 1912 and 1957, and the Moon between 1972 and 19—??

The science-fiction writers, and the pioneers of astronautics, have imagined human settlements on all the worlds of the Solar System – and even in space itself. They have dreamed that we will extend our commerce beyond the atmosphere, into the final frontier (to coin a phrase). And if anyone thinks that this idea is fantastic, let me remind him or her that half a century ago a single man in the Atlantic sky was headline news. How many thousands are up there at this very moment, dozing through the in-flight movie?

The analogy may be false; perhaps there is nothing in space to attract more than the occasional scientific mission or asteroid mining consortium. And even if the Solar System is full of opportunity, it may be argued that the enormous cost of escaping from the Earth will always place a severe limit on our ability to exploit extraterrestrial resources. Our great airports are already bad enough; even if we could afford it, do we really want a Space Shuttle taking off from somewhere on Earth every few minutes – and, almost as bad, booming back into the atmosphere?

Well, there is an alternative – and it's not anti-gravity, which may be impossible even in theory. It's the space elevator, or orbital tower, conceived in 1960 by the Russian engineer Yuri Artsutanov, and since re-invented at least five times.

For those of you who are not familiar with this at-first-sight preposterous idea, let me summarize briefly. It follows from the concept of stationary satellites, which everyone now takes for granted. Clearly, if a satellite can remain poised for ever above the same spot on the Equator, then in principle it should be possible to lower a cable from orbit to Earth, performing an Indian rope trick 22,000 miles high.

And if we can do that, we can go further. We can build an elevator system to send payloads into space without rockets, purely by electrical energy. This would totally transform the economics of space flight – as you will appreciate when I tell you that the cost, *in energy*, of carrying a man to the Moon is less than ten dollars.

The engineering problems are of course enormous, but extensive studies have found no fundamental flaw in the concept, which is now the basis of a rapidly expanding literature, to which I refer those who would like more details. Much ingenuity has now been applied to extending Artsutanov's basic idea, and it appears – surprisingly – that 'Skyhooks' or 'Jacob's Ladders' can be built to virtually any altitude, from any spot on the Earth – though at the cost of rather appalling mechanical complexities.

Whether these daring concepts will ever be realized in practice only the future will tell. But the imagination of the engineers has now opened up wholly new vistas in space, and also presents us with a beautiful paradox. On the small scale, space travel will always be extremely expensive. Yet if – and it's a big 'if' – it can ever be justified on a really massive scale, it could be one of the cheapest forms of transportation ever devised. Exactly as in the case of the familiar terrestrial elevator or lift, a space elevator would require very little energy to run – because the traffic moving downwards would lift that on the way up. Of course, the capital cost would be enormous; but a well-designed space elevator could last for centuries and would be an even better long-term investment than that other expensive but highly profitable tourist attraction, the Great Pyramid.

Perhaps you may consider that the space elevator puts too much of a strain on the imagination – but without imagination, nothing is ever achieved, as the history of astronautics amply proves. Yet it is possible to have too much of a good thing; uncontrolled imagination can be an even bigger menace than short-sighted conservatism, because it can lead to much greater disasters. I would like to conclude with two dreadful, or at least tragi-comic, examples of this in our own field of interest. One is past history; the other remains a continuing nuisance.

For almost two generations, the planet Mars was central in all discussions of extraterrestrial life, largely owing to the influence of one man, the American astronomer Percival Lowell. His dramatic claim to have discovered a network of apparently artificial 'canals' covering the planet generated millions of words of controversy – not to mention whole libraries of fiction.

We now know, thanks to the Mariner and Viking space probes, that the Martian canals are a total illusion, created in the mind's eye from the infinity of detail that can be glimpsed on the planet during the rare moments of good seeing. Yet Lowell – and many other astronomers! – drew them consistently for decades. How could this happen? The explanation, I suspect, runs something like this: Lowell was so determined to find intelligence on Mars that he created what he was looking for, as we have all done at some time or other. His drawings of Mars became more and more artificial, until eventually they looked like maps of the world's airlines. As an artist can do, he created a style – which was copied by others who were infected by his enthusiasm. More sceptical astronomers saw merely the natural patterns of light and shade which we now know represent the real Mars. The canals were a – shall we say – *infectious hallucination*, but to Lowell they were perfectly real.

His wealth and prestige – not to mention his considerable literary gifts – enabled him to sustain the illusion. When his very able assistant A. E. Douglass eventually became sceptical – *dis*-illusioned – and decided that the canals lay in the eye of the observer, what did Lowell do? He fired him – I am sure with genuine reluctance.

When Lowell died, so did the canals, though slowly. It took the Mariners and Vikings to inflict the final *coup de grâce*.

On a much larger scale, I am now convinced that something like this is responsible for the few UFO sightings that do not have trivial explanations. Let me devote a couple of minutes to the two cases which provided my own 'moments of truth' and which closed the subject as far as I am concerned – at least until some fundamentally new evidence comes along, which hasn't happened for twenty years . . .

In one famous incident, many eyewitnesses saw the classic spaceship, complete with lighted windows, flying a few thousand feet overhead. Some of them thought it had landed not far away. They weren't lying; they had indeed seen something unusual – and we know exactly what it was, without a shadow of doubt. It was not a spaceship a few miles up; it was a re-entering satellite at fifty times that altitude, burning up spectacularly in a trail of fire half-way across the sky. But the people who were expecting to see a spaceship, saw one. It was the Lowell Effect again.

There are so many hundreds of similar – and even more fantastic – misinterpretations, described *ad nauseam* in the literature, that I no longer waste any time on reports of strange things seen in the sky – even by competent observers. I've been fooled too often myself: one of my own half-dozen UFOs took weeks to identify. So my philosophy now is very simple, and based on that extremely rare commodity, common sense. Here is Clarke's Rule for dealing with a UFO: even if it does come from Proxima Centauri, but it doesn't stop, there's nothing you can prove one way or the other. So take pity on suffering humanity – *forget* it. Nothing will be lost; when there really *is* a landing, the fact will be established, without a shadow of doubt, within half an hour. We won't still be waving our arms thirty years later.

Then what about the hundreds of Close Encounters sometimes – though not always – reported by apparently sane and honest people?

Yes, it's the Lowell Effect again, in considerably more virulent form. My first glimpse of this obvious truth came when I was sent a book giving an account of a UFO kidnapping, full of drawings showing the spaceship and its occupants. I recognized the ship instantly; I'd known it for thirty years. And so has every American who's spent much time watching 'The Late, Late Show' . . .

Now, it is possible that a superior spacefaring civilization *may* base its design on 1950 Hollywood movies, but frankly I doubt it. Yet I don't doubt the honesty of the person who drew the sketches; they were no more faked than Lowell's maps of Mars. But they were also no *less* faked . . .

What clinched the matter, as far as I'm concerned, is the very recent discovery that some people can hallucinate so perfectly that even the electrical patterns in their brains agree with their visions. What this does to our concepts of reality I'm not quite sure. I hope I'm not hallucinating you. Or even worse – that you're not hallucinating me.

I'm sorry about this rather long digression – but UFOs are such an obstacle to serious discussions of life in space that perhaps you'll forgive me. And the theme of this talk is, after all, Imagination and Reality . . .

I would like to end by repeating, virtually unchanged, some words I addressed to the British Interplanetary Society in 1950 – seven years before the explosive dawn of the Space Age. After surveying the writings of the past, I posed this question: What will happen to tales of interplanetary adventure when space travel actually begins? Will they become extinct – as some foolish critics indeed predicted, the morning after Sputnik 1? This is what I said in that address:

When space travel is achieved, the frontier will merely shift outwards, and I think we can rely on the ingenuity of the authors to keep always a few jumps ahead of history. And how much more material they will have on which to base their tales! It should never be forgotten that, without some foundation of reality, science fiction would be impossible, and that therefore exact knowledge is the friend, not the enemy, of imagination and fantasy. It was only possible to write stories about the Martians when science had discovered that a certain moving point of light was a world. By the time that science has proved or disproved the existence of Martians, it will have provided hundreds of other interesting and less accessible worlds for the authors to get busy with.

So perhaps the interplanetary story will never lose its appeal, even if a time should come when all the Cosmos has been explored and there are no more universes to beckon men outwards across infinity. If our descendants in that age are remotely human, and still indulge in art and science and similar nursery games, I think that they will not altogether abandon the theme of interplanetary flight – though their approach to it will be very different from ours.

To us, the interplanetary story provides a glimpse of the wonders whose dawn we shall see, but of whose full glory we can only guess. To them, on the other hand, it will be something achieved, a thing completed and done countless aeons ago. They may sometimes look back, perhaps a little wistfully, to the splendid, dangerous ages when the frontiers were being driven outwards across space, when no one knew what marvel or what terror the next returning ship might bring – when, for good or evil, the barriers set between the peoples of the Universe were irrevocably breached. With all things achieved, all knowledge safely harvested, what more, indeed, will there be for them to do, as the lights of the last stars sink slowly towards evening, but to go back into history and relive again the great adventures of their remote and legendary past?

Yet we have the better bargain: for all these things still lie ahead of us.

— 5 —

Where the Action Is

This and the two subsequent chapters are taken from 'Beyond Apollo', the Epilogue which I had the great honour to contribute to the astronauts' own account of their mission, First on the Moon, *in 1970.*

Some years ago, a *New Yorker* cartoonist made a profound and witty observation on the nature of life. He drew a primeval beach, lined with the giant ferns that have long since vanished from the Earth. Crawling up out of the ocean was a clumsy, archaic fish – a coelacanth, or a close relative – while a few yards to the rear a companion lingered nervously in the deeper water. The intrepid adventurer, already half on dry land, was looking back at his anxious colleague. And he was saying, with a rather patronizing expression, 'Because this is where the action is going to be, baby.'

If such a prediction had really been made, half a billion years ago, it would have been remarkably accurate – but there would have been very little evidence to justify it. From the point of view of any fish, the land is a most unpleasant, hostile place. One would have to be crazy to explore it – and as for *living* there . . .

Look at the disadvantages. In the sea, there is no such thing as weight; a hundred-foot whale floats as effortlessly as a one-inch jellyfish. On land, the relentless pull of gravity drags all creatures downwards from birth to death. Even when it fails to kill them outright, as it frequently does, it often cripples them through the physical defects it induces in bone and muscle.

The sea is also a far more benign environment than the land. It has none of the violent temperature extremes – ranging over more than 250 degrees Fahrenheit – which occur between the tropics and the poles. There is no fierce source of ultraviolet radiation overhead, which can burn and even kill an unprotected organism. And apart from rare submarine earthquakes, it is always calm; only the uppermost skin of the sea is ever disturbed by storms.

Yet despite this, life came out of the sea – its ancient birthplace – and conquered the alien land. In so doing, it opened up whole new possibilities of existence which we now take for granted, but which would not have been at all obvious even to a fish of human intelligence – could one imagine such a thing – back in the Cambrian period.

Because it has many parallels with our present situation, it is worth pursuing this fantasy a little further. A genius-type coelacanth, peering up through the wavering surface of the water at the dimly seen world of trees, mountains, clouds, volcanoes, thunderstorms, could have made a good case for exploring this strange environment in the cause of science. He could have confidently, and correctly, pointed out that a wealth of new knowledge would come from such an investigation. He might have argued, 'How can we possibly understand our Universe while we are restricted to one small portion of it?' And, slightly anticipating Marshall McLuhan, he might even have realized that he could not hope to study water – until he had left it behind him.

But not even the most brilliant and far-sighted of fish could have imagined the ultimate consequences of the exploration – and colonization – of the land. He could not have anticipated the rise of new life forms, with much superior senses and greatly improved ability to manipulate the environment. Long-range vision, and the dexterity of human fingers, could never have evolved in the sea. Nor, in fact, could higher intelligence itself – simply because the benevolent sea does not provide the same challenges as the fierce and inhospitable continents. (Today's intelligent marine animals, the whales and dolphins, are of course all dropouts from the land.)

But, above all, our Palaeozoic Leonardo could never have imagined the new technologies which would be discovered and exploited once life had escaped from the all-embracing sea. In particular, the very existence, and the infinite uses, of fire would have been utterly beyond his comprehension. The taming and control of fire is the essential breakthrough which leads to the working of metals, to prime movers, to electricity – to everything, in fact, upon which civilization depends. Though an underwater culture is not inconceivable, it would be forever trapped in the Stone Age.

There is no need to pursue the analogy further; the lesson is obvious. When we escape from the ocean of air, we will be moving out into a whole universe of new sensations, experiences, technologies – only a few of which we can foresee today. Zero-gravity research, industry and medicine, open up such immense vistas that our descendants will find it impossible to believe that we ever managed without them. Yet the greatest boons from space, it is fairly certain, will come from discoveries still undreamed-of today. Waiting for us beyond the atmosphere are the equivalents, and perhaps the successors, of fire itself.

Prometheus stole the sacred flame from heaven and brought it down to Earth as a gift to the human race; and on a pillar of flame man is now riding back into the abode of the gods. What other divine powers still remain there for us to discover – and to exploit?

When we regard space exploration from this point of view, we can see at once the ludicrous short-sightedness of those who have regarded it merely as a competition between two ephemeral political entities of the late second millennium. It is true that the 'Space Race' was a fact of life in the 1960s, but the rivalry between Spain and Portugal was about as important – and as transient – in an earlier age of exploration.

There are some who may agree with these long-range historical, and evolutionary, implications of space travel, but would argue that they are so far in the future that they do not concern practical politics – that has to deal with the down-to-earth problems of transportation, housing, education, medical care, poverty, and so forth. Until these matters are settled, they ask, have we any right to throw billions of dollars into space?

There are so many answers to this question that it is difficult to know where to begin. At the most elementary level, it may be necessary to point out to some of the more naïve critics that the 24 billion dollars devoted to the space programme was not spent on a kind of astronomical foreign aid programme. It was all fed back into American industry, where it generated skills, hardware and technologies which in the long run will be worth far more than they cost – though it may be impossible to prove this beyond question for some years, just as no one could prove in 1903 that the Wright brothers had not wasted their entire investment. Moreover, much of the vast payroll of the space programme has been injected into the more backward areas of the United States. The chambers of commerce concerned may not care to advertise the fact, but it could be claimed with some justice that the Apollo project did more to drag certain states into the twentieth century than a great many programmes of direct social improvement.

There is a superficial reasonableness about another very common criticism of space expenditure. If one is determined to spend 24 billion dollars, surely it could be better used to build schools, hospitals, homes, roads – or to pay higher salaries to teachers, policemen and other underprivileged public servants?

Yet indirectly, as we have pointed out, it has helped to do just this. How much more efficient the process would have been had the amount been devoted entirely to this purpose could be argued endlessly – but the discussion would be a complete waste of breath, for it would have no connection with the realities of political life. It has often been remarked that money 'saved' from one worthwhile project cannot be switched to another, but has to be voted all over again – which in fact seldom happens.

The 'spaceships or schools' argument is a particularly unfortunate example of this fallacious reasoning. Indeed, the space programme is one of the best things that ever happened to the United States educational system, both financially and psychologically. The shock of Sputnik – America's technological Pearl Harbor – focused attention on schools and colleges in a way that nothing else could possibly have done.

Until 4 October 1957, even Admiral Rickover was a voice crying in the wilderness; after that date, education became a number-one priority, and suddenly the money became available. The very requirements of the space programme created an unprecedented demand for highly qualified men, and NASA was to become a major supporter of university research. Far from space robbing the schools and colleges, it contributed both directly and indirectly to their financial well-being. One can sympathize with those irate scholars who see millions being devoted to space research when they cannot get modest grants for their own pet projects; but they should realize that cutting space expenditure is much more likely to reduce their chances than to increase them. Budget-slicing is a contagious disease.

Moreover, the inspirational value of the space programme is probably of far greater importance to education than any input of dollars. No one who has lectured extensively to young people can have any doubts of this, though it may not be realized by those elderly academics who, as is well known, are careful to have little contact with students. But a whole generation is growing up which has been attracted to the hard disciplines of science and engineering by the romance of space. This body of trained men will, in the years to come, be one of the world's greatest assets, and no price can be put upon it. The starry-eyed youngster of today, watching TV broadcasts from the Moon, will be the inventor, discoverer or technical administrator of tomorrow. And it is worth pointing out, even at some risk of invoking the horrid spectre of the 'two cultures', that he will be among the students least likely to set fire to the dean's office, exchange fisticuffs with the campus police, or generally go to pot . . .

Individuals, as well as societies, need goals to inspire them; otherwise their existence becomes pointless, and the realization of that fact (whether consciously or unconsciously) results in those psychological and social ills with which we are all too familiar. And however much that mythical creature, the hard-headed, practical man-in-the-street may resent the fact, the most inspiring goals often have no obvious connection with the problems of everyday life.

The supreme physical achievement of the age of Pericles is the Parthenon; the foundations might still be unlaid had Phidias been compelled to justify his construction programme by the improvements that would eventually result in Athenian housing. It is quite possible that such a 'spin-off' did occur – but what does it matter? For more than two thousand years, the marble columns standing on the Acropolis have been among the most precious treasures of mankind – though doubtless the *hoi polloi* would have preferred better drains.

A few days after the first landing on the Moon, this point was excellently made by the London *Economist* – a very down-to-earth journal, not noted for imaginative flights of fancy. In its editorial for 26 July 1960, *The Economist* remarked:

And as the excitement dies and familiarity sets in, the voices that say the money could be better spent on ending wars and poverty on earth must gain converts.

But this argument overlooks the factor in human make-up that sets us apart from the apes. When man first became a tool-maker, he ceased to be a monkey. The human race's way of sublimating its highest aspirations has been to build the greatest and grandest artifact that the technology of the time can achieve. Through the pyramids, the parthenons and the temples, built as they were on blood and bones, to the be-spired cathedrals conceived and constructed in ages of great poverty, the line runs unbroken to the launch pad of Apollo 11. Oddly – or perhaps not so oddly – the churchmen with their unstinting praise of the astronauts have recognized this where the liberally educated rationalists with their bored carping, and their ill-bred little jokes, have not. Spiralling to the planets expresses something in human nature that relieving poverty, however noble a cause that is, does not. And to the planets, sooner rather than later, man is now certain to go.

Unlike the pyramids and the cathedrals, the exploration of space will have so many practical justifications that our descendants will think us mad that we ever doubted its value. But they will remember us, when all the creations of our hands have passed away – because we were the first men to set our sign among the stars, and our feet upon the Moon.

— 6 —

The Solar Century

From 'Beyond Apollo' *(1970).*

During the week of the first lunar landing, there was a sudden change of focus of the human imagination. Until then, the Moon had been the limit of most men's thoughts; that we might soon walk on its surface – though accepted as a logical possibility – was something that the mind could not really grasp. Then, almost in a moment, dream became reality; Armstrong and Aldrin might have explored no more than a few square yards of the Sea of Tranquillity, but no one could doubt that the entire Moon had now come within reach. Its exploration, and perhaps its colonization, was only a matter of time.

In a few dazzling hours, a once mythical world had become real estate. And because the human spirit must always have fresh goals, the new frontiers of the imagination swept overnight out to the planets. Men began to speak of Mars as only months before they had spoken of the Moon.

Some of this talk was uninformed speculation – post-Apollo euphoria – by those who had no idea of the technical problems involved. It might almost be compared with the hopes ignorantly expressed, at the end of the eighteenth century, by the people who believed that now men had risen into the air by the newly invented balloon, they could easily fly on to the Moon. It was not quite as simple as that; the lunar voyage had to wait for another two hundred years . . .

This time, however, the popular reaction was somewhat more in accord with the facts. Although – even at its nearest – Mars is almost a hundred and fifty times further away than the Moon, in frictionless space distance is no measure of difficulty. Once a rocket has escaped from the Earth's gravitational field, which it has to do even to reach the neighbouring Moon, it requires very little extra fuel to travel on to Mars, Venus, or indeed any of the planets.

The chief problem in manned interplanetary travel is not propulsion, but life support.

If we employ the orbits which require the minimum fuel – as we will be compelled to do in the early days of exploration – the very shortest round trips will last about two years. This means that we must preserve life in space for a hundred times the duration of a lunar journey; thus vast improvements in our present systems are required. One of the most important functions of manned space stations will be to test and develop methods of air and temperature control, as well as food regeneration which can be relied on for periods of years. This can be done safely in an environment which is only a few hours' flight time away from Earth; if anything goes wrong, one can come home in a hurry. This would not be true, half-way to Mars . . .

Even when we are fairly confident of our techniques, it would be rash to set out for Mars or Venus in a single spacecraft. When he sailed for the New World, Columbus very wisely used three ships. That would be a reassuring number for our early interplanetary expeditions.

Before we go to the planets, we will know far more about them than we do today, when most of our ideas are still little better founded than the early speculations about the Moon. Powerful telescopes in orbit, and TV cameras carried on space probes like the Mariners and Voyagers, will have dispelled much of our present ignorance. But there is no substitute for a man on the spot, and in the case of the planets there is another reason – often overlooked by those who advocate purely robot explorations – why we must eventually send our eyes and brains across the abyss.

We can, and probably will, examine much of the Moon with the aid of unmanned 'lunar rovers' under radio control from Earth. But the Moon is only *two and a half seconds* away by radio waves; there is time to react to emergencies (such as rocks or crevasses in the line of travel) or to take advantage of those unexpected opportunities which are the essence of successful exploration.

Such operation in real time will be quite impossible on the planets. Even when Mars is at its closest, a radio signal takes five minutes for a one-way journey. If one of our Martian rovers got into trouble, it would be ten minutes before our corrective instructions could reach it, fifteen before we could know if we had done the right thing, twenty before we could change our minds. And this is the minimum time lag; for the outer planets the delay would be several hours. Though we will be able to give our robot explorers a great deal of autonomy, so that they can look after themselves in most foreseeable situations, when it comes to really strange and hostile environments it will be essential to have human controllers only a second or so away – that is, in orbit around the planet being explored, if not actually on its surface.

A striking example of the limitations of robot scouts was given by Dr Ernst Stuhlinger of the Marshall Space Flight Center in January 1967, when, with Dr Wernher von Braun and Dr Robert Gilruth, he visited the US Antarctic Base to get a better understanding of the problems of interplanetary exploration. They were shown around by one of the local biologists who

pointed out to us the various forms of algae and arthropods that live in that region, and he described their ingenious ways of adaptation to this unusual environment. Each rock sample which he selected with the trained eyes of the research biologist contained on its protected underside some specimens of algae, mites or small insects; the samples which we untrained space engineers picked up did not show any traces of life. 'No wonder,' said Dr [Russell] Strandtmann. 'This is the difference between a live, alert, intelligent, highly trained and motivated scientist, and a lifeless robot. Do you see now,' he added, 'why we scientists believe that man should go in person to the Moon and to Mars?'

When nuclear propulsion is perfected, it will be easier (and cheaper) to reach the nearer planets than it is now to travel to the Moon. And as our technology continues to advance, the velocities we can attain will steadily rise. Flight times will drop from months to weeks – and ultimately to mere days. We will be able to travel anywhere we wish in the Solar System, and visit all the children of the Sun.

Some of those are very strange offspring indeed. Yet perhaps we had better get used to the fact that *our* planet is the anomaly, with its hard, cold rocks and its unique, oxygen-bearing atmosphere. Any explorers from interstellar space might overlook it completely during their first examination of the Solar System; they might notice only the four 'gas giants' Jupiter, Saturn, Uranus and Neptune. Compared with these monstrous worlds the so-called terrestrial planets Earth, Mars, Venus and Mercury are insignificant dwarfs, huddling round the warmth of the central Sun.

It is almost half a billion miles to Jupiter, and nearly three billion to Neptune, the outermost of the giants. Yet despite the unimaginable distances involved, we have an opportunity of examining *all four* of these worlds within the next two decades – using the launch vehicles we already possess. An automatic probe aimed toward Jupiter in 1977 could swing past that planet in 1979 and, if its timing was correct, could get a boost from the Jovian gravity field which would flick it on to Saturn. Here the same thing would be repeated when it arrived in 1981, and four years later it would reach Uranus. Cannoning off a third gravitational field in this game of cosmic billiards, it would arrive at Neptune in 1989, after a total flight of twelve years. Although this may seem a long time – and it will pose some very severe problems to the electronics designers – the direct flight *to Neptune alone* would normally take twenty years.

Opportunities for this multiple mission (the 'Grand Tour') occur only in the period 1976–8. Thereafter, the planets will not get lined up properly again for 175 years. It will be a pity if we miss the best chance to survey all the giant planets this side of the year 2153.

Even by that date, it seems unlikely that we will have got very far in unravelling the mysteries of Jupiter, the lord of them all. Mere statistics cannot convey the sheer size of Jupiter; it means little to say that the planet has 11 times Earth's diameter and 318 times its mass. There is one mental image, however, that does give a faint impression of Jovian magnitude. If some cosmic collector of worlds skinned our planet and pinned its pelt like a game trophy on the face of Jupiter, it would appear there about as large as India on a terrestrial globe. In other words, Jupiter is to Earth as Earth is to India; anyone who has ever flown over the endless plains of that country may well feel numb at the thought of exploring Jupiter.

However, it is by no means certain if Jupiter has a solid surface to be explored. All we can see through our telescopes are the outer layers of a colourful and extremely turbulent atmosphere which consists largely of hydrogen, methane and ammonia. The rapid spin of the planet – despite its size, its rotation period is only ten hours – produces trade winds that must make ours seem like gentle zephyrs; the resulting immense belts of cloud, parallel to the Equator, give Jupiter a characteristic banded appearance.

The nature of these clouds, if that is the appropriate term for them, is a major mystery. Hydrogen, methane and ammonia are quite colourless – yet the Jovian atmosphere shows a wide range of pinks and blues and salmons. Its most conspicuous feature, the thirty-thousand-mile-long oval known as the Great Red Spot, has even been described as brick-red, though sometimes it fades (or sinks?) to invisibility.

Because it is at five times the Earth's distance from the Sun, Jupiter might be expected to be extremely cold; this is certainly true of its upper atmosphere. However, recent observations indicate that it is not quite as cold as it should be; like our own planet, Jupiter appears to have internal sources of heat. Some tens or hundreds of miles below the clouds it may be warm enough for water to exist in the liquid form; and given sufficient time, water plus hydrocarbons plus energy may add up to life.

A generation ago, practically all scientists would have dismissed the idea of life on Jupiter as absurd, owing to the 'poisonous' nature of its atmosphere. But we now realize that this is a very naïve and self-centred viewpoint; modern biological theories suggest that the ancient Earth, some four billion years ago, had a gaseous envelope much like Jupiter's – and it was in such an atmosphere that primitive life first arose. Only at a much later stage, when plants evolved, were the hydrogen-bearing compounds methane and ammonia replaced by oxygen; not until then could animal life appear. It is oxygen which is a deadly poison to primitive organisms – and, indeed, even to man if the pressure is increased too greatly.

Jupiter may, therefore, be in the very early stages of biological evolution; this could explain some of the extraordinary colours in its atmosphere, typical of many complex organic compounds. Whether this is fantasy or an exciting reality, we should know very soon, thanks to astronomical instruments in Earth orbit. But it will be a very long time before we can actually send instruments – or men –

down into that witch's brew of an atmosphere, stirred by storms and fertilized by bolts of lightning more powerful than any on Earth.

The three other giants – Saturn, Uranus and Neptune – appear to be quite similar to Jupiter, except that they are considerably smaller and much less active. (But even the smallest, Neptune, is three and a half times the diameter of Earth!) Saturn, however, has one unique* and famous characteristic: its beautiful set of rings, which form a kind of multiple halo in the planet's equatorial plane. Although they appear solid when viewed through a telescope, the rings are actually composed of small particles in independent circular orbits. They are probably dust and ice; it may not be too far from the truth to say that Saturn is surrounded by a perpetual hailstorm.

The four giant planets possess 29 known moons between them, and there must be many others still undiscovered.† Jupiter (12 satellites) and Saturn (10) are almost small solar systems in themselves; indeed, some of their moons are comparable in size to the planets Mars and Mercury. However, because of their great distances, they appear as little more than pinpoints even in our most powerful telescopes. We can only assume that they are frozen, lifeless hunks of rock and ice.

Even so, they may have many surprises – and at least one of these worlds already presents us with a tantalizing mystery. Iapetus, the ninth moon of Saturn, is about six times brighter on one side of its orbit than on the other. There must be some remarkable formation – almost a giant natural mirror – flashing sunlight back at us from certain angles of illumination.

Saturn's largest moon, Titan, is sufficiently massive to hold an atmosphere – a tenuous one – of methane gas.‡ Any atmosphere is useful for braking purposes, and methane is a particularly valuable substance, since it is 25 per cent hydrogen. One day, our nuclear rockets may refuel here; Titan may be the key to the outer planets and beyond.

---

*No longer unique – Jupiter, Uranus and Neptune also possess rings; but they are pathetic compared with Saturn's.

†How true! The latest total is 57 – Jupiter 16, Saturn 18.

‡False, alas! Titan's atmosphere is denser than Earth's – and at least 90 per cent nitrogen.

Until well into the next century, however, most of our manned explorations will be directed to smaller, more Earthlike planets closer to the Sun. Mercury, Venus and Mars all lie within a few months' flight time, even by today's slow-moving spacecraft, and they are all solid bodies, upon which it will be possible to make landings. Whether it will be desirable to do so is quite another matter.

Mercury, so close to the Sun that the radiation it receives is ten times more powerful than on Earth, may closely resemble the Moon. Too small to retain an atmosphere, it is so hot that metals could melt in its equatorial regions. During a century of observation, astronomers had convinced themselves that the little planet keeps the same face always turned toward the Sun, as the Moon does toward the Earth. Thus a whole science-fiction mythology had arisen, describing a world one side of which was frozen in perpetual night, while the other burned for ever beneath a pitiless Sun.

To the great embarrassment of astronomers, radar observations showed in 1965 that this simple, Dantesque picture is just not true. Mercury does know day and night, like any well-appointed planet; it spins on its axis once every 59 days. This does little to alleviate its climate, but the extremes of heat and cold encountered there do not present a serious problem to space technology. Moreover, by a careful choice of latitude and time, it would be possible to find landing areas on Mercury where – for periods of several weeks – Earthlike temperatures occurred.

There can be no doubt that men will one day visit Mercury, if only to install or service automatic monitoring equipment. Whether permanent bases will ever be established there is a question that only the future can decide. The reasonable assumption is that such a blistering lump of rock will have few resources and fewer attractions, except to a handful of devoted astrogeologists.

But nature is infinitely varied, and there may be much more on Mercury than we can possibly imagine today. For one thing, it seems to have an inexplicably high density – as if, for some peculiar reason, it is a repository of heavy metals. Commenting on this, the British mathematician R. A. Lyttleton recently informed the Royal Astronomical Society that 'Mercury may well be the strangest planet in the Solar System.' This is a startling assertion; perhaps we should not write off this little world too quickly as an unimportant lump of rock.

However, not even those hardy optimists, the science-fiction writers, really expect to find any form of life on Mercury. Although it is not too difficult to imagine organisms that could survive there (particularly underground, where the temperature would be moderate), if the planet never possessed oceans, biological evolution could not have started. Yet again, we are talking of life as we know it; we should prepare ourselves for the discovery that we know very little about it indeed.

Of all the planets, the one for which we had the highest hopes was Venus. Almost a twin of Earth in size, with a gravity very slightly weaker so that it would produce a mild buoyancy, Venus also comes closer to the Earth (26 million miles) than any other body, except for the Moon and a few stray planetoids – wandering mountains about the size of Central Park. Though it is considerably nearer to the Sun than our world, its permanent covering of brilliant white clouds reflects 90 per cent of the solar heat back into space. For this reason, it was hoped that its temperature would not be excessively high. Nowhere else in the Solar System seemed a more likely abode of life; the dazzling cloud cover at once evoked images of oceans and rain-drenched forests, perhaps trampled by great beasts like those that our own planet knew in the days of the dinosaurs.

Alas for these dreams! One by one we have been forced to relinquish them. First the spectroscope revealed that the atmosphere contains huge quantities of the suffocating gas carbon dioxide – which precluded any form of animal life, but did not eliminate plants. Then Earth-based measurements of the radiation from the planet indicated that it was far hotter than anyone had imagined; so hot, in fact, that water could exist there only in the form of steam.

For a few years ingenious theories 'explained away' these observations, but the last faint hopes for a merely tropical Venus were shattered by the Mariner 2 fly-by of 1962, and finally laid to rest by the Russian Venera probes of 1969. As these descended into the atmosphere, they registered not only very high pressures (comparable to those a thousand or more feet down in our oceans) but temperatures of 800 degrees Fahrenheit. Conditions on the surface of Venus appear roughly similar to those inside a blast furnace.

That still leaves Mars, beloved by romantic writers for almost a hundred years, largely thanks to the report in 1877 of a network of fine lines (the so-called canals) covering the surface of the planet like the map of an international airline system. It is now known that the canals are illusory; although there are some rather diffuse linear features, Mars in close-up is no more artificial-looking than the Moon. In fact, as the brilliantly successful Mariners 4, 6 and 7 showed, it very closely resembles the Moon, being covered with craters of all sizes up to at least a hundred miles in diameter.

Yet there is one all-important difference between Mars and the Moon – and that is the presence of an atmosphere. That Mars has an atmosphere had been known for almost two centuries, because its surface features are occasionally obscured by mists or clouds. However, it is not an atmosphere which we could possibly breathe, for it contains virtually no oxygen. Even if it were pure oxygen, it would still be useless to us – for it is much thinner than the air on the summit of Mount Everest.

Nevertheless, any atmosphere, as long as it is not an actively poisonous one, is probably better than none. The tenuous Martian atmosphere acts as an effective screen against the small meteorites that might otherwise pepper the planet's surface, and it moderates the temperature extremes. It may also help to circulate the small (but possibly vital) amount of water vapour that exists on Mars.

The public attitude toward Mars has oscillated between extremes of pessimism and optimism, as a kind of over-reaction to each new advance in knowledge. When the Mariner TV cameras showed a bleak, cratered landscape, there was an immediate assumption that the planet had now been proved to be lifeless. This was absurd; much better pictures of Earth, from considerably shorter ranges, have shown no signs of life here! This question may not be settled even when we have landed robot probes on Mars, as Dr Stuhlinger's experience in the Antarctic demonstrates. Once again we are faced with the difficult problem of proving a negative. If there is life on Mars, the proof may be obtained within a decade, or even less; but if there is not, it may take a century of careful examination to demonstrate this beyond doubt. Though large and active life forms could hardly be overlooked, it seems likely that anything surviving in such a rugged environment would be small, inconspicuous, and restricted to a few favoured locations.

It might also have to be mobile to avoid the long, ferocious winters: although on a summer afternoon the equatorial temperature may rise to the seventies, the average temperature is below freezing point – and the minimum may be 200 degrees below zero Fahrenheit. But Mars is a small world – half the diameter of Earth – and its year is almost twice as long; moreover, it has no seas to act as barriers to migration. Thus any creature which could travel a modest five miles per day need never experience winter.

It is said that a famous astronomer once received this message from William Randolph Hearst: 'Is there life on Mars? Please cable one thousand words.' He got the reply, 'Nobody knows' – repeated five hundred times. Now at last there is a chance of a more informative answer. And if it should be 'No', that will only be temporary. In what is, from the astronomical viewpoint, a mere flicker of time, there will be life on Mars – and perhaps most of the other planets and their satellites. It will have come from Mother Earth.

The Shores of Infinity

From Beyond Apollo *(1970).*

The story of man has been one of expanding horizons; even today, there are a few Stone Age cultures where the limits of the unknown are only a dozen miles away.

First by land, thanks to conquerors and travellers like Alexander the Great and Marco Polo, the world widened. Yet not until the development of the sailing ship, and the arts of navigation, did Columbus, Magellan and their successors reveal the true lineaments of the globe. The fantastic cosmographies of the Dark Ages, with their mythical realms and monsters, lost their power over the minds of men. For the last four hundred years, every educated person has lived in essentially the world our parents knew.

But not the world *we* know. In one brief decade, our imaginations have had to encompass the Moon. We can pinpoint the very moment when it ceased to be a heavenly body and became a place; it was 23 November 1966, when Lunar Orbiter 2 radioed back to earth the historic photograph of the Copernicus crater – and for the first time we looked not upon but *across* the landscape of another world.

In a few more years, we will experience the same revelation with Mars, Mercury, Venus . . . Before the end of this century, the entire Solar System will have become the background of our lives, as robot probes penetrate to its farthest reaches, and men prepare to follow them. Human thought will undergo another change of scale, comparable to that which occurred during the first Age of Discovery, half a millennium ago.

But for all the obvious parallels, there will be a profound difference between these two eras. Columbus and his fellow-navigators were filling in the details of a world which, though large, they knew to be finite. The men of the twenty-first century will always be aware that, far beyond their widest voyaging, the stars and galaxies are scattered across a volume of space which is unimaginably large, and may indeed be infinite.

There is a familiar household object which gives a good idea of the scale of the Solar System, and of the gulfs beyond. Take an ordinary 12-inch LP record,* and imagine that the hole in the centre is the Earth's orbit 180 million miles wide. Then Pluto lies on the rim and all the outer planets are scattered across the disc; Saturn is at the edge of the label.

As yet, we have just started to explore the hole in the middle, which contains the Sun, Mercury and Venus, and have sent a few probes a tenth of an inch outwards towards Mars. The remainder is still unknown, though already within our reach if we are prepared to spend years in silent coasting through space.

On this scale, the very nearest of the stars – and therefore the closest possible system of other planets – is three-quarters of a mile away. Our Sun is a barely visible speck of dust, one of a hundred thousand million which on the average are about a mile apart. The whole collection of suns (the Galaxy) forms a disc about five times the diameter of Earth. Even with this drastic reduction, our model has got a little out of hand . . .

It is not surprising, therefore, that we do not know if there are any other solar systems besides our own. Across gulfs which shrink the sun itself to a feeble star, even a giant planet like Jupiter is utterly invisible. Nevertheless, there is indirect evidence that a few of the neighbour stars do have dark, planet-sized companions, and today most astronomers think it likely that the majority of suns possess solar systems. From this, it is an easy step to assume that planets bearing life – and intelligence – are commonplace throughout the Universe.

This is probable; the alternative – that this tiny Earth is the only inhabited planet in a Cosmos of at least 10,000,000,000,000,000 million suns seems the wildest fantasy one can imagine. But at this stage of our knowledge there is no proof whatsoever that any life, or any intelligence, exists beyond the Solar System. Some scientists, rashly ignoring the lessons of the past, have denied that such proof

*This certainly dates the essay! Still, most people will remember what an LP looks like . . .

will ever be obtained; they feel that the distances involved present an insuperable barrier to knowledge. And they ridicule the idea that living creatures – men or other beings, should they exist – can ever span the abyss between the stars.

The development of space flight itself shows how dangerous it is to make such negative predictions. Moreover, in this case they can be shown to be false, at least to a high degree of probability. There may indeed be absolute bars to interstellar travel – but if so, they must be based on factors not yet known. What is already certain is that there are no serious difficulties in establishing interstellar communication – always assuming, of course, that there is someone to talk to at the other end . . .

The quite amazing development of radio astronomy during the last thirty years has given us all the technology required. The gigantic antennas designed to catch faint, natural signals from the depths of space, and the sensitive receivers to amplify them, are the very tools needed for this task. In barely more than half a century since Marconi flashed his first signals across the Atlantic (a feat then widely declared to be impossible!) we have developed equipment with which we can talk to the stars.

No one has yet tried to do this, though there have been limited attempts to listen for intelligent messages from space. If these are ever discovered, it is likely to be as a by-product of some radio-astronomical investigation, because no one is going to tie up millions of dollars' worth of equipment on a random search that may last for decades – or centuries – with no certainty that it will ever meet with success. The detection of the extraordinary pulsars occurred in just such a fashion; at first, their trains of accurately timed radio pulses appeared to fit exactly the specifications of intelligent signals. Now it seems that they can be explained as a natural, though very surprising, phenomenon; the sharply defined pulses may be produced by spinning 'neutron stars' – dense bodies only a few miles in diameter, yet weighing as much as the Sun.

To be quite certain that we are receiving intelligent signals, we must prove that they carry some kind of message, even if it is not one that we can interpret. So far, there is no indication that the pulsars – or any other sources of radiation in space – are doing this. That discovery might come at any moment, and would have a shattering impact upon human philosophy, religion and perhaps even politics. The mere knowledge that another intelligence existed somewhere else in the Universe would affect our thoughts and our behaviour in a myriad subtle ways. At the very least, it might cause our quarrelsome species to close its ranks.

Beyond this, the possibilities are so numerous that speculation is limited only by the laws of logic. Just a few of the questions that might arise are: Does the message contain any useful information? (It would be possible to transmit a cosmic encyclopaedia, and an advanced, benevolent civilization might do so.) Should we attempt to answer? (It might not be worth it; if the message came from the Andromeda galaxy, it would have been on its way since the first ape men experimented with clubs. On the other hand, if it came from one of the nearer stars, our reply could be received in a decade or so.) And perhaps most interesting of all: Is the source approaching? ('We shall be landing on the White House Lawn/Red Square in thirty minutes . . .')

The theme of cosmic confrontation is, of course, the classic stand-by of the science-fiction writers, but it is now time that we took it seriously. (In the past it has sometimes been taken too seriously, as in 1938 when Orson Welles' *War of the Worlds* radio play spread panic across the eastern US seaboard.) Some writers have expressed perhaps premature thanks for the existence of 'God's quarantine regulations', which may allow us to communicate across the interstellar distances, but which will prohibit any form of physical contact.

It is true that the distances involved in flight to the stars are about a million times greater than those which must be crossed to reach the planets; but this does not imply a proportionate increase in difficulty. It is a surprising fact that a Saturn 5 could send a payload of many tons clear out of the Solar System – to reach, for example, Sirius. But it would take a few hundred thousand years to get there.

However, this is at the very beginning – the log-canoe stage – of our space technology, which will advance beyond recognition in the centuries to come. There is no theoretical reason why speeds which are a substantial fraction of the velocity of light may not be ultimately achieved, at least by robot probes on one-way missions. This would make the closer stars perhaps twenty years away, and it would be surprising if, during the next few centuries, we do not attempt to send successors of today's Mariners and Voyagers to the nearest stellar systems.

But what of manned flight? It has been said that interstellar travel is not an engineering problem, but a biological one. Certainly, biological techniques – known or foreseeable – give a number of possible solutions.

One is the multi-generation starship, a mobile, self-contained worldlet which might cruise for centuries, until the descendants of the original voyagers made planetfall in a new solar system. Another way of arriving at the same result would involve suspended animation (hibernation); if this proves to be impossible with human beings, then we might send frozen ova, which were automatically fertilized a couple of decades before the end of the voyage. The children thus born could be reared by robot nurses, and in due course introduced to their distant heritage of human knowledge and history.

If this particular idea sounds nicely calculated to bring a gleam of maniacal delight to the eyes of Dr Strangelove, can anyone doubt that we would attempt it, if the Sun was about to explode and we had the time and the technology thus to make our race immortal? The Galaxy is full of detonating stars – how many doomed races may already have tried such desperate experiments? As already remarked, our island Universe, the Milky Way system, contains a hundred thousand million stars. Equally significant is the fact that it has existed for at least five thousand million years – that is, more than a million times the duration of human history. Over such expanses of space and time, anything that is technically possible has probably been achieved not once, but over and over again. There may be innumerable cosmic arks, making their lumbering way between the stars . . .

It is possible that even interstellar travel may not be particularly time-consuming – at least, from the viewpoint of the travellers themselves. As is widely known, though imperfectly understood, Einstein's theory of relativity predicts that as velocities approach that of light (186,000 miles a second, or 670 million miles an hour) time itself appears to slow down.

This prediction has been experimentally verified with high-speed atomic particles, and has fascinating consequences for space travellers. It means (in theory at least) that journeys of any distance are possible during the span of a human life, and indeed in as short a period of time as may be desired, if there is enough power to give the necessary speed and the crew can withstand the acceleration involved. To give a concrete example (taken from Shklovskii and Sagan's book *Intelligent Life in the Universe*), one can imagine a spaceship setting out for the Andromeda galaxy at a constant acceleration of one gravity, so that the crew would experience their normal weight. If this acceleration could be maintained, the crew would be 28 years older when the ship arrived at Andromeda.

Now this is very surprising – because light takes about two million years to make the same journey, and nothing can exceed the speed of light! Yet no contradiction is involved. From the point of view of outside observers, the spaceship never quite attains the speed of light, and so the voyage lasts a full two million years. But to the travellers – and all their clocks, since everything in the ship is equally affected – only 28 years would have elapsed. They would have no way of telling that anything peculiar had happened to them, unless they turned around and went straight home. Then, 56 years older, they would land on an Earth where four million years had passed . . .

If anyone asks, 'How long did the voyage really take?', the answer is that both figures are correct – it all depends on the observer. One day, this 'time-dilatation' phenomenon may cause little more surprise than the fact that it can be noon in New York, when it is 5 p.m. in London.

A trip to Andromeda is a rather extreme case, but journeys to the neighbouring stars, out to a few dozen light-years away, do not appear quite so far-fetched; for example, the bright star Vega (distance 26 light-years) could be reached in about 6 years of ship time and the 12-year-older crew could return home 52 years after they had left. This would give them at least a sporting chance of seeing their children again . . .

Unfortunately, the levels of power and energy needed for these interesting feats are of such a magnitude that we do not know, even in theory, how they may be attained. The ultimate form of nuclear propulsion, involving the total conversion of mass into thrust with

100 per cent efficiency (which is certainly impossible) would be utterly inadequate, and power outputs comparable to those of the Sun would be needed for the more ambitious relativistic missions.

Because of this, some scientists have argued that velocities approaching that of light can never be attained, no matter how far present or foreseeable methods of propulsion are improved. This conclusion is probably correct – but it is about as useful and relevant as a demonstration that no wooden, coal-burning airplane can ever make a supersonic crossing of the Atlantic.

It is absurd to imagine that the energy sources, and the methods of employing them, which we can envisage here at the very dawn of the Neotechnic Age are those that will still be employed a thousand years from now. Even at the beginning of this century, who would have dreamed of the 200 million horsepower that lift the Saturn 5? It is doubtful, in fact, if so much power was then available to the entire human race.

To state that the energy of a whole sun would be needed to drive a starship does not prove the impossibility of such a vehicle. It merely means that we may have to wait a few centuries before we can build one – which, perhaps, is desirable for a number of excellent reasons.

Nor should we be discouraged by the undoubted fact that nuclear energy – the most concentrated source of power now known – is wholly inadequate for high-speed star faring. Recent astronomical discoveries strongly suggest that nuclear power is pretty feeble stuff, compared to some of the forces being let loose in the Cosmos. When we observe 'quasars' or radio galaxies liberating energies equivalent to the simultaneous explosion of a billion stars, we may well wonder if we are glimpsing some new order of creation. Fifty years ago, studies of the Sun gave us our first hint of the powers locked in the hydrogen atom, which we have now released – though not yet tamed – here on Earth. One day we may likewise learn the secrets of the quasars; and if we survive that knowledge, we will be on our way to the stars.

Whether we shall be setting forth into a Universe which is still unbearably empty, or one which is already full of life, is a riddle which the coming centuries will unfold. Those who described the first landing on the Moon as man's greatest adventure are right;

but how great that adventure will really be we may not know for a thousand years.

It is not merely an adventure of the body, but of the mind and spirit, and no one can say where it will end. We may discover that our place in the Universe is humble indeed; we should not shrink from the knowledge, if it turns out that we are far nearer the apes than the angels.

Even if this is true, a future of infinite promise lies ahead. We may yet have a splendid and inspiring role to play, on a stage wider and more marvellous than ever dreamed of by any poet or dramatist of the past. For it may be that the old astrologers had the truth exactly reversed, when they believed that the stars controlled the destinies of men.

The time may come when men control the destinies of stars.

— 8 —

The First Scouts

From Beyond Jupiter – The Worlds of Tomorrow, *the 1972 collaboration with the eminent architect, astronomer and painter Chesley Bonestell.*

In the late 1960s the space mission planners, with something of a shock, suddenly realized that the key to the outer planets lay within their grasp.

A few nineteenth-century astronomers had found that comets occasionally disappeared from the Solar System as a result of an encounter with Jupiter. The gravitational field of the giant planet could, under the right conditions, produce a kind of slingshot effect, boosting the speed of a body passing close by. Thus a comet which came near to Jupiter could be accelerated right out of the Solar System. What was true of Jupiter was also true, to a slightly lesser degree, of Saturn and the other giants. They could *all* give a 'free gravity assist' to spacecraft approaching along suitable orbits.

The possibility arose of arranging what was promptly christened a 'Grand Tour' across the Solar System. If the necessary standards of reliability and navigational accuracy could be attained, we could fly a space probe to Jupiter, let Jupiter flick it on to Saturn, Saturn to Uranus, and so on.

In space research, as in ordinary life, it is impossible to do everything that is worth while: one has to decide on priorities, and this is often an agonizing business. There was never any chance that NASA would be able to conduct *all* the Grand Tour missions, and early in 1972 it was decided that the development of the Space Shuttle would take precedence over outer-planet exploration. Some limited missions beyond Jupiter may be carried out by the United States; but just which still remains to be seen. For NASA, the Grand Tour has, alas, become the Economy Tour.

It would be impossible to make serious plans for missions covering billions of miles, and lasting many years, without a vast body of previous experience in space technology, much of it acquired the hard way. Behind the Grand Tour concept lie several generations of increasingly more sophisticated – and reliable – space probes: Ranger, Mariner, Orbiter, Surveyor . . .

Although the earlier writers on astronautics were quite correct in their ideas about propulsion, structures, fuels and the main engineering aspects of space flight, they could not anticipate the electronic revolution, which made it possible to perform feats surely beyond their wildest dreams. Thus when Robert Goddard, in his classic Smithsonian paper 'A Method of Reaching Extreme Altitudes' (1919), discussed the problem of proving whether or not a rocket had actually reached the Moon, the only solution he could suggest was that it should carry a few pounds of flash powder, to be ignited on contact. (He calculated that less than fourteen pounds would be strikingly visible in a 12-inch telescope, against the unilluminated surface of the Moon.) When Luna 2 performed this feat just forty years later (on 13 September 1959), it was followed by radio all the way, and the increase in its velocity right up to the very second of impact was accurately measured by the Doppler effect* of the returning waves.

The technology of tracking spacecraft by radio was first developed for the Vanguard satellite in the late 1950s; the ability to get information back from distant, moving objects is very much older. The art of 'telemetering' goes back to the weather-balloon 'radiosondes' with which meteorologists started exploring the atmosphere in the 1930s. These skills, and many others, were already at hand when the time was ripe to send probes to the planets, but they would not have been practical without another development – the rise of solid-state electronics. The transistor and its still smaller successors started to replace the bulky, fragile and power-consuming vacuum tube at just the right time.

Electronic equipment that, in the 1940s, would have filled a room, had shrunk to shoebox size by the mid-1960s. By the 1970s, it

*Familiar from the change in pitch of a locomotive whistle as a train passes by. A similar shift of frequency occurs with radio waves and gives an extremely sensitive measurement of velocity.

was no larger than a matchbox – and was still contracting. It must be admitted that the demands of long-range missilery, rather than the search for knowledge, had wrought these miracles; but they were there, waiting for the space scientists to use them when they were required.

The first objective was, of course, the Moon. (We are really very fortunate to have a large, interesting heavenly body so close at hand; how discouraging to be a Venusian* astronaut, with the nearest land 25 million miles away – a hundred times the distance of the Moon!)

The robot exploration of our single natural satellite began in 1959 with the USSR's Luna 3, which took the first photographs of the hidden far side of the Moon. Although they were very crude, they gave astronomers a tantalizing initial glimpse of a land that had once been the very symbol of everything that could never be known. Surprisingly, it was six years before a second view of the far side was obtained, from the Russian 'Automatic Space Station' Zond 3 (July 1965).

Before then, however, a series of nine Ranger spacecraft had been launched by the United States, in an attempt to learn something about the fine details of the lunar surface. After a heartbreaking series of six failures, Ranger 7 (July 1964) worked perfectly, and televised more than four thousand pictures back to Earth before it crashed into the Sea of Clouds. The last picture was taken from a distance of less than half a mile, and brought the Moon a thousand times closer than it could be observed through any Earth-based telescope. Rangers 8 and 9 (February and March 1965) brought the project to a triumphant conclusion; it was during the final mission that the dramatic words LIVE FROM THE MOON appeared for the first time on television. The last photographs transmitted by Ranger 9 before it destroyed itself on impact showed objects less than a foot across. Only a year earlier, the limit of resolution for Earth-based telescopes had been a mile.

And a year later, there was another huge advance, when Luna 9 and Surveyor 1 (January and May 1966) made the first soft landings

---

*The classicists have had a field day over this. Hesperian, Cytherean, Venutian have all been proposed. Venusian is as bad as Earthian, but we are probably stuck with both.

on the Moon, and their cameras showed the detailed, close-up texture of the surface. Their touchdowns demolished many theories and exorcized many imaginary perils – particularly the long-feared lunar dust, into which it was once confidently predicted that spacecraft would sink without trace.

The Rangers, Lunas and Surveyors could examine only a limited region of the Moon, and what was also needed was a global mapping project which would cover the entire surface from pole to pole. To do this would obviously require a camera in orbit.

The USSR tackled the problem with its Zond series of spacecraft. Zond 5 (September 1968) was the first object to circle the Moon and return safely to Earth. It carried an aerial mapping camera – not a TV camera – so the film was recovered and processed, as in a normal air reconnaissance mission.

This technique, repeated in later Zond flights, has a good deal to recommend it because there is nothing to match the quality of an original photograph. But since it demands physical recovery of the spacecraft (or at least of the film capsule) it has severe limitations, and obviously cannot be used for long-range interplanetary missions. In such cases, all information – scientific data, instrument readings, pictures, spacecraft performance figures – has to be sent back by radio.

Between August 1966 and August 1967, the United States launched a series of five Lunar Orbiter spacecraft, which among them photographed virtually the entire surface of the Moon – front and back – at ten or more times the resolution obtainable from the best telescopes on Earth. So climaxed three hundred years of patient effort, by thousands of amateur and professional astronomers, to map the face of the Moon. This is not to say that ground-based observations are no longer of any value, and the recording of surface details remains an endlessly fascinating hobby. Indeed, it could be argued that observation of selected regions by experts has become even more important – and may be much more rewarding now that they know exactly what they are looking at. Until there is a *permanent* orbital patrol of the Moon, there is still no substitute for Earth-based observers.

The superb Orbiter photographs were sent back to Earth by a combination of photographic and electronic techniques known as 'film readout'. The images of the Moon were photographed on a long roll of special film, which was processed aboard the spacecraft. When the film had been developed and fixed, the images were scanned, line by line, by an extremely small spot of light. A photocell 'read off' the reflected light, and the resulting signal was radioed back to Earth, where it was a straightforward matter to reconstruct the original image.

Among the highlights of the Orbiter missions were the famous photograph of Copernicus – the first portrait of the lunar world – and the mapping of the sites for all the Apollo landings. The astronauts would never have been able to make their exploring trips, especially the long-distance traverses in the Lunar Rovers, without the beautiful photographs provided by the Orbiters.

While the Moon was disgorging its secrets, space probes had also been launched to the two nearest planets, Mars and Venus. On 14 December 1962, Mariner 2 became the first spacecraft to radio back information from another planet when it flew past Venus at a distance of 22,000 miles. It carried no picture-taking equipment, but it obtained valuable scientific information and confirmed the hypothesis – which many scientists had been reluctant to subscribe to – that Venus is extremely inhospitable. The last doubters were convinced when the USSR's Venera 4 succeeded in dropping an instrument-carrying capsule into the planet's atmosphere on 18 October 1967; it was crushed by the unexpectedly high pressure while still some twenty miles above the surface.

Venera 4 had been preceded by at least eleven failures; the Russian deep-space effort has been far more ambitious than the American one, and started much earlier, with one probe being aimed at Mars as early as October 1960. It was not until December 1970 that Venera 7 penetrated the full thickness of the atmosphere and broadcast from the almost red-hot surface of Venus for twenty minutes, before succumbing to heat stroke.

However, Mars had always been regarded as a more promising objective, especially from the photographic point of view. Unlike Venus, it was not perpetually shrouded in clouds; its thin atmosphere (incorrectly believed, before the 1960s, to have about one-tenth the density of Earth's) seldom obscured the surface details which had intrigued and tantalized astronomers for more than a hundred years.

The first TV camera was flown past Mars on 14 July 1965, aboard Mariner 4, and radioed back 21 pictures of quite limited resolution. Nevertheless, they were full of surprises, and overnight most existing theories about Mars became obsolete. There was no sign, alas, of the famous 'canals', and at first sight the planet which had been the home of so many romantic fantasies seemed as cratered and lifeless as the Moon. Mariner 4 also established that the Martian atmosphere was ten times thinner than anyone had imagined – only about one-hundredth the density of Earth's. In its more modest way, Mars looked almost as unpromising as Venus, though not quite so ferociously hostile.

In July and August 1969 two considerably more advanced spacecraft, Mariners 6 and 7, obtained many more photographs and mapped a sizeable fraction of the planet during the few hours of their fly-bys. But it was clear that – as in the case of the Moon – what was wanted was a spacecraft that could remain in orbit, making observations for weeks or months. This was the only economical way to study the planet as a whole and to monitor any variations that might be taking place. For Mars, unlike the Moon, is a dynamic world, with weather, seasonal changes, and waxing and waning polar caps.

The new era of Martian observations began in November 1971, with the first interplanetary orbiter – Mariner 9. (There should have been a Mariner 8, but it had been destroyed a few minutes after launch by the failure of a component, too small to be visible to the naked eye, in one of the control circuits.) Mariner 9 made a perfect lift-off on an Atlas-Centaur from Cape Kennedy on 30 May. For more than five months it coasted, like an independent planet of the Sun, along the arc of a great ellipse; and on 13 November it overtook Mars. (*See next chapter.*)

Appointment with Mars

Like the preceding chapter, this comes from Beyond Jupiter – The Worlds of Tomorrow *(1972).*

The Ranger, Orbiter and Mariner projects have all been supervised by the Jet Propulsion Laboratory (JPL) of the California Institute of Technology, and some of the greatest scientific triumphs (and disasters) of the Space Age have been witnessed in its Mission Control Center. On the afternoon of 13 November 1971, a number of scientists and journalists gathered in the visitors' viewing room to witness the Mariner 9 encounter with Mars.

The weather that day was perfect. For once, the Pasadena hills were visible; there was not a trace of the infamous Los Angeles smog, and we could see with crystal clarity for thirty miles. In a few more hours this was to be the subject of ironic comment.

Like the gallery of a theatre, the viewing room overlooked the Mission Control Center and was separated from it by a large, soundproofed window. The general layout of the Center, with its flickering TV monitors, glowing lights, digital clocks counting seconds up *and* down, and large visual displays, was very similar to the Mission Control Center in Houston, but the scale of things was slightly smaller. The knowledge that men's lives were not involved reduced the tension, but the feeling of suspense was still considerable. At stake were more than a hundred million dollars, countless thousands of the most skilled man-hours in the world and the only chance, for several years, to multiply at least tenfold all that had ever been learned about Mars in the centuries since men had studied the planet. Probably no one had forgotten the fate of Mariner 9's precursor, now attracting inquisitive fish somewhere on the Atlantic sea-bed.

But Mariner 9 had now covered 248 million miles in five months, and was still operating flawlessly. Forty-eight hours earlier, while the spacecraft was some half-million miles from the planet, its two TV cameras had been switched on, and their pictures of Mars had been played back to Earth. They had shown, as expected, a small, featureless disc, like the Moon about three days from full, so it was known that the camera system was operating normally.

The large TV monitor screens in the viewing room now displayed rows and columns of numbers which, to the initiated, gave a complete analysis of the spacecraft's state of health. Dozens of readings of temperature, voltage, gyro angles, propellant pressure and other more esoteric quantities were being continually taken, converted into digital pulses, and beamed back to Earth with a power of only twenty watts – about that of the feeblest light bulb. Seven minutes later, travelling at 186,000 miles a second, an almost infinitesimal fraction of that energy arrived at the great 210-foot tracking antenna at Goldstone, California.

Amplified, cleaned up and decoded, the pulses were converted into numbers and displayed on the monitors, thus telling the engineers everything they needed to know about Mariner 9, now so far from its builders. Most of these numbers did not change for hours at a time, because the spacecraft was still in cruise mode, its energies stored up and waiting for their moment of release.

Mariner 9 was racing in towards Mars, still accelerating in the planet's gravitational field, at over 11,000 miles an hour. If unbraked, the probe would make a right-angle turn around Mars at a height of some 800 miles, and then go into orbit around the Sun. To become a third moon of Mars, it would have to reduce its speed by 3,600 miles an hour, otherwise the planet could never capture it.

About two hours before the encounter with Mars, Goldstone had beamed the sequence of pulses which told the spacecraft's computer, 'Initiate manoeuvre sequence.' The signal was repeated four times – just to make sure that it was heard. If, for some reason, there had been a breakdown in communications with Earth, the central computer would have gone ahead anyway at the correct time. All essential instructions had been given to it in advance, but Mission Control could change them if necessary. Mariner 9 had to have a great deal of independence since it would take seven minutes for any orders to reach it – and the ground controllers could not know for another seven minutes if they had been obeyed.

During the next two hours, the spacecraft made its preparations for the rendezvous. The autopilot was switched on; the tiny gyros – which measured the vehicle's orientation in space and told it where it was pointing at any moment – were given ample time to build up speed. All the electrical systems warmed up, drawing power from the four solar panels, which made the spacecraft look rather like an old-fashioned windmill. They could extract about 500 watts of energy from the sunlight falling on them; when the vehicle went into shadow behind Mars, it had enough reserve battery power to keep operating during the period of eclipse.

At 3.52 p.m., Pacific Standard Time (PST), the lines of numbers on the Mission Control monitors suddenly started to change. Seven minutes earlier, out at the orbit of Mars, the roll jets had fired.

An observer flying along with the spacecraft would not have noticed the feeble puffs of nitrogen gas from the thimble-sized micro-rockets at the tips of the solar sails. But he would have seen that the windmill was slowly turning – very slowly – taking four minutes to rotate through less than half a right angle, as if its vanes were responding to a barely perceptible breeze. However, they soon came to rest again.

Eight minutes later, the entire windmill started to slew around, as if searching for a more favourable compass bearing. This time, it swung through more than a right angle and took twelve minutes to reach its new position. But the vanes, with their thousands of solar cells glinting like rubies in the sunlight, still refused to turn.

What the spacecraft had done was to orientate itself so that its main rocket motor was pointing in the direction of flight, while its radio antenna was aimed back at Earth. It was now in the correct position for retrofire; 800 miles below, the surface of Mars was rolling backwards at 11,000 miles an hour.

For the scientists and engineers at JPL, now was the moment of truth. The propulsion system was a new one, never before tested in space; its rocket engine must run flawlessly for sixteen minutes, consuming almost half a ton of the reactive liquids nitrogen tetroxide and methyl hydrazine. Though these are not the most powerful of fuels, they possess one overwhelming advantage for a mission such as this: they burn spontaneously on contact, so there is no need for vulnerable ignition systems or pyrotechnics to set them off.

It was now very quiet in the viewing room; all of us were watching the monitors and conversation had stopped completely. From time to time I glanced at Dr Pickering, who appeared remarkably relaxed and cheerful. I wondered if he was thinking of Ranger 6, which had flown a perfect trajectory all the way to the Moon – with a camera system that turned out to be dead when it arrived . . .

Suddenly, there was a ripple of cheers and an outburst of clapping. At 4.24 p.m. (PST), the line of telemetry numbers indicating motor-chamber pressure had started to flicker. The motor was firing, delivering its full 300 pounds of thrust. We could relax then – partially. The propulsion system still had to operate for 16 minutes, cutting Mariner's speed by almost a mile a second, before the spacecraft could enter the desired orbit around Mars.

The telemetered figures on the monitors continued to bring in good news; the thrust was steady, the gyros were holding the correct attitude. Now, no one could believe in the possibility of failure; even though the spacecraft was not yet in the correct orbit, it had lost so much speed that Mars was bound to capture it. Some kind of reconnaissance could be carried out, and in the back rooms of Mission Control all sorts of emergency and contingency plans were happily discarded.

At 4.20 p.m., precisely on time, chamber pressure and thrust dropped to zero as the motor ceased firing. Mariner 9 was in a long, elliptical orbit which would take it around Mars in just over twelve hours; later, the orbit would be trimmed by a short burn which would make the period exactly 11.98 hours. This odd figure had been chosen to suit spacecraft photography; every seventeen Mars-days, the cameras would look down on the same areas, at the same sun elevation. Only in that way would it be possible to ensure that any changes in appearance were real, and not due merely to varying shadows.

Mariner would start to take its first photos from orbit early next morning (Sunday), while it was making a pass over the south pole. At the rate of one every 42 seconds, it would store 33 pictures in its little video-tape recorder, and would beam them back to Earth about an hour later. This first playback, however, was going to be somewhat tedious: each picture would require three-quarters of an hour to come through – six times longer than its coded pulses would take on the trip from Mars to Earth! During its transmission, therefore, every picture would be spread out along a band 45 light-minutes, or 500 million miles, long. Even this slow rate of acquisition was a great improvement on the performance of the first Mariner to reach Mars; then, it had taken an agonizing eight hours to build up every picture.

Now, thanks to greatly improved electronic techniques, the eight hours had been cut to either forty-five minutes or six minutes, depending on the Earth station in use. Only the huge 210-foot dish at Goldstone could collect enough power to permit the six-minute rate of reception; when the spin of the Earth no longer allowed the Goldstone dish to be pointed at Mars, smaller 65-foot dishes in Spain, South Africa and Australia had to be used, and these required forty-five minutes per picture. Mariner would always be visible from at least one of these radio telescopes – the heart of NASA's Deep Space Network.

Goldstone was back in action by 2.00 p.m. on Sunday afternoon, and the pictures began coming in at the high rate. As each frame started to arrive, every line of the scan would be counted, and the corresponding line numbers 1, 2, 3 . . . began to appear on the monitor. There were 700 lines to a scan, so excitement would mount toward the high 600s, when each new image was almost due. At 700, the monitor would flash 'Line Scan Complete' and go blank for a few seconds, while the computer did the final assembly of the image. And then Mars would flash on the screen.

It must be admitted that those first images were a considerable disappointment. By a very odd – some thought suspicious – coincidence, Mars had become as coy as Venus, just when we were about to have our closest look. The entire surface of the planet was covered with cloud; one of the greatest storms ever observed was raging over the daylight side. Someone in Misson Control put up a cartoon showing the Martians sucking the still strangely absent Los Angeles smog across space and using it to camouflage their world.*

---

*A document was later circulated at JPL in which the Martian equivalent of the CIA claimed credit for this obscuration. Authorship has been attributed to me. Like any good spook, I deny everything.

This was very frustrating to the geologists and cartographers, and still more so to the news networks, who wanted to have some good pictures. But in the long run – assuming that Mariner functioned for its planned ninety-plus days – it would probably be a piece of luck. As they watched the storm die away, the meteorologists would learn much more about the behaviour of the Martian atmosphere than if all had been calm and peaceful. And how fortunate that the earlier fly-by Mariners 4, 6 and 7 had not arrived at such a time! They had had only a few hours in which to make their observations; this Mariner could afford to wait for weeks.

On some images, distinct dark patches appeared – perhaps mountain peaks jutting above the cloud layer. There was a considerable amount of detail that just eluded the eye, and this could be exaggerated by 'computer enhancement'. Just as, on a TV set, one can produce a falsely dramatic image by turning the contrast all the way up, so the computers could process the image – dot by dot – revealing contours of light and shade which the naked eye could not possibly perceive. The result had to be studied with caution; sometimes the enhancement put in things that simply weren't there.

Since each picture embodied five and a half million 'bits' of information (700 lines, 832 picture elements per line, 9 bits per picture element), the computation involved in this was awesome. In fact, the entire mission would have been utterly impossible before the advent of high-speed computers, for during its orbital operations Mariner demanded some 36 billion calculations a day. With old-style desk machines, this would have required one-quarter of the entire labour force of the United States.

Even if the television experiments had to bide their time, the other measurements were already coming in splendidly. Mariner carried three other instruments – one spectrometer for the ultra-violet, another for the infra-red, and an infra-red radiometer (or detector) which would map the temperature of the planet with great precision.

The spectrometers should produce a wealth of information about the composition of the Martian atmosphere and surface; the radiometer should locate any hot spots, which could be a sign of internal activity and might suggest promising places to look for life.

All three instruments were pouring back torrents of raw data and covering yards of recording paper with pen tracks which conveyed meaning only to specialists; and even the specialists would need months to interpret them.

I managed to gatecrash one of the first meetings in which all the principal scientific investigators had gathered to exchange and interpret their results, and to make plans for the next day's operations. It was an impressive collection of talent, covering many disciplines and including one Nobel Prize winner (Dr Joshua Lederberg). The atmosphere was one of good humour and excited anticipation.

Although I understood almost a tenth of what was going on, I cannot report on it; that is the rightly, and jealously, guarded privilege of the researchers concerned. There is an elaborate protocol for the publication of scientific results; anyone who jumps the gun and makes a premature disclosure is liable to be expelled from the club. It has happened.

Three days after Mariner had gone into orbit, the storm was still raging and only a few vague glimpses of the Martian surface had been obtained. But two weeks later, the TV cameras had their first chance of showing what they could really do.

From time to time, as Mariner raced around its twelve-hour orbit, it came within a few thousand miles of the tiny moons, Phobos and Deimos. In Earth's largest telescopes they appear no more than points of light, and were assumed to be irregular chunks of rock ten or fifteen miles in diameter. Mariner proved that this assumption was indeed true, showing the larger moon, Phobos, in amazing detail from a distance of 3,444 miles. Though not a very beautiful object, Phobos provided the first glimpse that man had ever had of a new type of heavenly body . . . perhaps part of the debris left over from the formation of the Solar System.

And one day, Phobos may be very important. There are a few billion tons of building material there, conveniently orbiting at the approaches to Mars. This little offshore island may be a meeting place for the commerce of the planets, in the centuries to come.

— 10 —

So You're Going to Mars?

This essay was published in Holiday *magazine (March 1953), long before the Mariner and Viking space probes gave us our close-up glimpses of the tantalizing red planet. Nevertheless, most of the concepts presented here are still quite valid, though we now know that Mars is even more rugged than anticipated. In particular, the atmospheric pressure is so low (about one-hundredth of Earth's) that simple breathing masks will not give sufficient protection; we will have to wear space suits.*

Many of the ideas in this article were worked out in much more detail in my novel The Sands of Mars *(1951).*

So you're going to Mars? That's still quite an adventure – though I suppose that in another ten years no one will think twice about it. Sometimes it's hard to remember that the first ships reached Mars scarcely more than half a century ago and that our colony on the planet is less than thirty years old. (By the way, don't use *that* word when you get there. Base, settlement, or whatever you like – but not colony, unless you want to hear the ice tinkling all around you.)

I suppose you've read all the forms and tourist literature they gave you at the Department of Extraterrestrial Affairs. But there's a lot you won't learn just by reading, so here are some pointers and background information that may make your trip more enjoyable. I won't say it's right up to date – things change so rapidly, and it's a year since I got back from Mars myself – but on the whole you'll find it pretty reliable.

Presumably you're going just for curiosity and excitement – because you want to see what life is like out on the new frontier. It's only fair, therefore, to point out that most of your fellow-passengers will be engineers, scientists or administrators travelling to Mars – some of them not for the first time – because they've got a job of work to do. So whatever your achievements here on Earth, it's advisable not to talk too much about them, as you'll be among people who've had to tackle much tougher propositions. I won't say that you'll find them boastful; it's simply that they've got a lot to be proud of, and they don't mind who knows it.

If you haven't booked your passage yet, remember that the cost of the ticket varies considerably according to the relative positions of Mars and Earth. That's a complication we don't have to worry about when we're travelling from country to country on our own globe, but Mars can be six times further away at one time than at another. Oddly enough, the shortest trips are the most expensive, since they involve the greatest changes of speed as you hop from one orbit to the other. And in space, speed, not distance, is what costs money.

Incidentally, I'd like to know how you've managed it. I believe the cheapest round trip comes to about thirty thousand dollars, and unless the firm is backing you or you've got a very elastic expense account . . . Oh, all right, if you don't want to talk about it . . .

I take it you're OK on the medical side. That examination isn't for fun, nor is it intended to scare anyone off. The physical strain involved in space flight is negligible – but you'll be spending at least two months on the trip, and it would be a pity if your teeth or your appendix started to misbehave. See what I mean?

You're probably wondering how you can possibly manage on the weight allowance you've got. Well, it can be done. The first thing to remember is that you don't need to take any suits. There's no weather inside a spaceship; the temperature never varies more than a couple of degrees over the whole trip, and it's held at a fairly high value so that all you'll want is an ultra-lightweight tropical kit. When you get to Mars you'll buy what you need there and dump it when you return. The great thing to remember is *only carry the stuff you actually need on the trip*. I strongly advise you to buy one of the complete travel kits – a store like Abercrombie & Fitch can supply the approved outfits. They're expensive, but will save you money on excess baggage charges.

Take a camera by all means – there's a chance of some unforgettable shots as you leave Earth and when you approach Mars. But there's nothing to photograph on the voyage itself, and

I'd advise you to take all your pictures on the outward trip. You can sell a good camera on Mars for five times its price here – and save yourself the cost of freighting it home. They don't mention that in the official handouts.

Now that we've brought up the subject of money, I'd better remind you that the Martian economy is quite different from anything you'll meet on Earth. Down here, it doesn't cost you anything to breathe, even though you've got to pay to eat. But on Mars the very air has to be synthesized – they break down the oxides in the ground to do this – so every time you fill your lungs someone has to foot the bill. Food production is planned in the same way – each of the cities, remember, is a carefully balanced ecological system, like a well-organized aquarium. No parasites can be allowed, so everyone has to pay a basic tax which entitles him to air, food, and the shelter of the domes. The tax varies from city to city, but averages about ten dollars a day. Since everyone earns at least ten times as much as this, they can all afford to go on breathing.

You'll have to pay this tax, of course, and you'll find it rather hard to spend much more money than this. Once the basic needs for life are taken care of, there aren't many luxuries on Mars. When they've got used to the idea of having tourists around, no doubt they'll get organized, but as things are now you'll find that most reasonable requests won't cost you anything. However, I should make arrangements to transfer a substantial credit balance to the Bank of Mars – if you've still got anything left. You can do that by radio, of course, before you leave Earth.

So much for the preliminaries; now some points about the trip itself. The ferry rocket will probably leave from the New Guinea field, which is about two miles above sea level on the top of the Orange Range. People sometimes wonder why they chose such an out-of-the-way spot. That's simple: it's on the Equator, so a ship gets the full thousand-mile-an-hour boost of the Earth's spin as it takes off – and there's the whole width of the Pacific for jettisoned fuel tanks to fall into. And if you've ever *heard* a spaceship taking off, you'll understand why the launching sites have to be a few hundred miles from civilization.

Don't be alarmed by anything you've been told about the strain of blast-off. There's really nothing to it if you're in good health – and you won't be allowed inside a spaceship unless you are. You just lie down on the acceleration couch, put in your earplugs, and relax. It takes over a minute for the full thrust to build up, and by that time you're quite accustomed to it. You'll have some difficulty in breathing, perhaps – it's never bothered me – but if you don't attempt to move you'll hardly feel the increase of weight. What you will notice is the noise, which is slightly unbelievable. Still, it lasts only five minutes, and by the end of that time you'll be up in the orbit and the motors will cut out. Don't worry about your hearing; it will get back to normal in a couple of hours.

You won't see a great deal until you get aboard the space station, because there are no viewing ports on the ferry rockets and passengers aren't encouraged to wander around. It usually takes about thirty minutes to make the necessary steering corrections and to match speed with the station; you'll know when that's happened from the rather alarming 'clang' as the air locks make contact. Then you can undo your safety belt, and of course you'll want to see what it's like being weightless.

Now, take your time, and do exactly what you're told. Hang on to the guide rope through the air lock and don't try to go flying around like a bird. There'll be plenty of time for that later: there's not enough room in the ferry, and if you attempt any of the usual tricks you'll not only injure yourself but may damage the equipment as well.

Space Station One, which is where the ferries and the liners meet to transfer their cargoes, takes just two hours to make one circuit of the Earth. You'll spend all your time in the observation lounge: everyone does, no matter how many times they've been out into space. I won't attempt to describe that incredible view; I'll merely remind you that in the hundred and twenty minutes it takes the station to complete its orbit you'll see the Earth wax from a thin crescent to a gigantic, multicoloured disc and then shrink again to a black shield eclipsing the stars. As you pass over the night side you'll see the lights of cities down there in the darkness, like patches of phosphorescence. And the stars! You'll realize that you've never really seen them before in your life.

But enough of these purple passages; let's stick to business. You'll probably remain on Space Station One for about twelve hours, which will give you plenty of opportunity to see how you like weightlessness. It doesn't take long to learn how to move around; the main secret is to avoid all violent motions – otherwise you may crack your head on the ceiling. Except, of course, that there isn't a ceiling since there's no up or down any more. At first you'll find that confusing: you'll have to stop and decide which direction you want to move in, and then adjust your personal reference system to fit. After a few days in space it will be second nature to you.

Don't forget that the station is your last link with Earth. If you want to make any final purchases, or leave something to be sent home – do it then. You won't have another chance for a good many million miles. But beware of buying items that the station shop assures you are 'just the thing on Mars'.

You'll go aboard the liner when you've had your final medical check, and the steward will show you to the little cabin that will be your home for the next few months. Don't be upset because you can touch all the walls without moving from one spot. You'll only have to sleep there, after all, and you've got the rest of the ship to stretch your legs in.

If you're on one of the larger liners, there'll be about a hundred other passengers and a crew of perhaps twenty. You'll get to know them all by the end of the voyage. There's nothing on Earth quite like the atmosphere in a spaceship. You're a little self-contained community floating in vacuum millions of miles from anywhere, kept alive in a bubble of plastic and metal. If you're a good mixer, you'll find the experience very stimulating. But it has its disadvantages. The one great danger of space flight is that some prize bore may get on the passenger list – and short of pushing him out of the air lock there's nothing anyone can do about it.

It won't take you long to find your way around the ship and to get used to its gadgets. Handling liquids is the main skill you'll have to acquire: your first attempts at drinking are apt to be messy. Oddly enough, taking a shower is quite simple. You do it in a sort of plastic cocoon, and a circulating air current carries the water out at the bottom.

At first the absence of gravity may make sleeping difficult: you'll miss your accustomed weight. That's why the sheets over the bunks have spring tensioning. They'll keep you from drifting out while you sleep, and their pressure will give you a spurious sensation of weight.

But learning to live under zero gravity is something one can't be taught in advance: you have to find out by experience and practical demonstration. I believe you'll enjoy it, and when the novelty's worn off you'll take it completely for granted. Then the problem will be getting used to gravity again when you reach Mars!

Unlike the take-off of the ferry rocket from Earth, the break-away of the liner from its satellite orbit is so gentle and protracted that it lacks all drama. When the loading and instrument checks have been completed, the ship will uncouple from the space station and drift a few miles away. You'll hardly notice it when the atomic drive goes on; there will be the faintest of vibrations and a feeble sensation of weight. The ship's acceleration is so small, in fact, that you'll weigh only a few ounces, which will scarcely interfere with your freedom of movement at all. Its only effect will be to make things drift slowly to one end of the cabin if they're left lying around.

Although the liner's acceleration is so small that it will take hours to break away from Earth and head out into space, after a week of continuous drive the ship will have built up a colossal speed. Then the motors will be cut out and you'll carry on under your own momentum until you reach the orbit of Mars and have to start thinking about slowing down.

Whether your weeks in space are boring or not depends very much on you and your fellow-passengers. Quite a number of entertainments get organized on the voyage, and a good deal of money is liable to change hands before the end of the trip. (It's a curious fact, but the crew usually seems to come out on top.) You'll have plenty of time for reading, and the ship will have a good library of microbooks. There will be radio and TV contact with Earth and Mars for the whole voyage, so you'll be able to keep in touch with things – if you want to.

On my first trip, I spent a lot of my time learning my way around the stars and looking at clusters and nebulae through a small telescope I borrowed from the navigation officer. Even if you've never felt the slightest interest in astronomy before, you'll probably be a keen observer before the end of the voyage. Having the stars all around you – not merely overhead – is an experience you'll never forget.

As far as outside events are concerned, you realize, of course, that absolutely nothing can happen during the voyage. Once the drive has cut out, you'll seem to be hanging motionless in space: you'll be no more conscious of your speed than you are of Earth's seventy thousand miles an hour around the Sun right now. The only evidence of your velocity will be the slow movement of the nearer planets against the background of the stars – and you'll have to watch carefully for a good many hours before you can detect even this.

By the way, I hope you aren't one of those foolish people who are still frightened about meteors. They see that enormous chunk of nickel-steel in New York's American Museum of Natural History and imagine that's the sort of thing you'll run smack into as soon as you leave the atmosphere – forgetting that there's rather a lot of room in space and that even the biggest ship is a mighty small target. You'd have to sit out there and wait a good many centuries before a meteor big enough to puncture the hull came along. It hasn't happened to a spaceship yet.

One of the big moments of the trip will come when you realize that Mars has begun to show a visible disc. The first feature you'll be able to see with the naked eye will be one of the polar caps, glittering like a tiny star on the edge of the planet. A few days later the dark areas – the so-called seas – will begin to appear, and presently you'll glimpse the prominent triangle of the Syrtis Major. In the week before landing, as the planet swims nearer and nearer, you'll get to know its geography pretty thoroughly.

The braking period doesn't last very long, as the ship has lost a good deal of its speed in the climb outward from the Sun. When it's over you'll be dropping down on to Phobos, the inner moon of Mars, which acts as a natural space station about four thousand miles above the surface of the planet. Though Phobos is only a jagged lump of rock not much bigger than some terrestrial mountains, it's reassuring to be in contact with something solid again after so many weeks in space.

When the ship has settled down into the landing cradle, the air lock will be coupled up and you'll go through a connecting tube into the port. Since Phobos is much too small to have an appreciable gravity, you'll still be effectively weightless. While the ship's being unloaded the immigration officials will check your papers. I don't know the point of this; I've never heard of anyone being sent all the way back to Earth after having got this far!

There are two things you mustn't miss at Port Phobos. The restaurant there is quite good, even though the food is largely synthetic; it's very small, and only goes into action when a liner docks, but it does its best to give you a fine welcome to Mars. And after a couple of months you'll have got rather tired of the shipboard menu.

The other item is the centrifuge; I believe that's compulsory now. You go inside and it will spin you up to half a gravity, or rather more than the weight Mars will give you when you land. It's simply a little cabin on a rotating arm, and there's room to walk around inside so that you can practise using your legs again. You probably won't like the feeling; life in a spaceship can make you lazy.

The ferry rockets that will take you down to Mars will be waiting when the ship docks. If you're unlucky you'll hang around at the port for some hours, because they can't carry more than twenty passengers and there are only two ferries in service. The actual descent to the planet takes about three hours, and it's the only time on the whole trip when you'll get any impression of speed. Those ferries enter the atmosphere at over five thousand miles an hour and go half-way around Mars before they lose enough speed through air resistance to land like ordinary aircraft.

You'll land, of course, at Port Lowell: besides being the largest settlement on Mars it's still the only place that has the facilities for handling spaceships. From the air the plastic pressure domes look like a cluster of bubbles – a very pretty sight when the sun catches them. Don't be alarmed if one of them is deflated. That doesn't mean that there's been an accident. The domes are let down at fairly frequent intervals so that the envelopes can be checked for leaks. If you're lucky you may see one being pumped up – it's quite impressive.

After two months in a spaceship, even Port Lowell will seem a mighty metropolis. (Actually, I believe its population is now well over twenty thousand.) You'll find the people energetic, inquisitive, forthright – and very friendly, unless they think you're trying to be superior.

It's a good working rule never to criticize anything you see on Mars. As I said before, they're very proud of their achievements and after all you *are* a guest, even if a paying one.

Port Lowell has practically everything you'll find in a city on Earth, though of course on a smaller scale. You'll come across many reminders of 'home'. For example, the main street in the city is Fifth Avenue – but suprisingly enough you'll find Piccadilly Circus where it crosses Broadway.

The port, like all the major settlements, lies in the dark belt of vegetation that roughly follows the Equator and occupies about half the southern hemisphere. The northern hemisphere is almost all desert – the red oxides that give the planet its ruddy colour. Some of these desert regions are very beautiful; they're far older than anything on the surface of our Earth, because there's been little weathering on Mars to wear down the rocks – at least since the seas dried up, more than 500 million years ago.

You shouldn't attempt to leave the city until you've become quite accustomed to living in an oxygen-rich, low-pressure atmosphere. You'll have grown fairly well acclimatized on the trip, because the air in the spaceship will have been slowly adjusted to conditions on Mars. Outside the domes, the pressure of the natural Martian atmosphere is about equal to that on the top of Mount Everest – and it contains practically no oxygen. So when you go out you'll have to wear a helmet or travel in one of those pressurized jeeps they call 'sand fleas'.

Wearing a helmet, by the way, is nothing like the nuisance you'd expect it to be. The equipment is very light and compact and, as long as you don't do anything silly, is quite foolproof. As it's very unlikely that you'll ever go out without an experienced guide, you'll have no need to worry. Thanks to the low gravity, enough oxygen for twelve hours' normal working can be carried quite easily – and you'll never be away from shelter as long as that.

Don't attempt to imitate any of the locals you may see walking around without oxygen gear. They're second-generation colonists and are used to the low pressure. They can't breathe the Martian atmosphere any more than you can, but like the old-time native pearl divers they can make one lungful last for several minutes when necessary. Even so, it's a silly sort of trick and they're not supposed to do it.

As you know, the other great obstacle to life on Mars is the low temperature. The highest thermometer reading ever recorded is somewhere in the eighties, but that's quite exceptional. In the long winters, and during the night in summer or winter, it never rises above freezing. And I believe the record low is minus one hundred and ninety!

Well, you won't be outdoors at night, and for the sort of excursions you'll be doing, all that's needed is a simple thermosuit. It's very light, and traps the body heat so effectively that no other source of warmth is needed.

No doubt you'll want to see as much of Mars as you can during your stay. There are only two methods of transport outside the cities – sand fleas for short ranges and aircraft for longer distances. Don't misunderstand me when I say 'short ranges': a sand flea with a full charge of power cells is good for a couple of thousand miles, and it can do eighty miles an hour over good ground. Mars could never have been explored without them. You can *survey* a planet from space, but in the end someone with a pick and shovel has to do the dirty work filling in the map.

One thing that few visitors realize is just how big Mars is. Although it seems small beside the Earth, its land area is almost as great because so much of our planet is covered with oceans. So it's hardly surprising that there are vast regions that have never been properly explored, particularly around the poles. Those stubborn people who still believe that there was once an indigenous Martian civilization pin their hopes on these great blanks. Every so often you hear rumours of some wonderful archaeological discovery in the wastelands, but nothing ever comes of it.

Personally, I don't believe there ever *were* any Martians – but the planet is interesting enough for its own sake. You'll be fascinated by the plant life and the queer animals that manage to live without oxygen, migrating each year from hemisphere to hemisphere, across the ancient sea-beds, to avoid the ferocious winter.

The fight for survival on Mars has been fierce, and evolution has produced some pretty odd results. Don't go investigating any Martian life forms unless you have a guide, or you may get some unpleasant surprises. Some plants are so hungry for heat that they may try to wrap themselves around you.

Well, that's all I've got to say, except to wish you a pleasant trip. Oh, there *is* one other thing. My boy collects stamps, and I rather let him down when I was on Mars. If you could drop me a few letters while you're there – there's no need to put anything in them if you're too busy – I'd be much obliged. He's trying to collect a set of space-mail covers postmarked from each of the principal Martian cities, and if you could help – thanks a lot!

— 11 —

The Winds of Space

In this essay, first appearing in book form in 1966, the facts on which various questions are based have not been superseded by recent discoveries, and seem just as valid today and just as stimulating as a basis for discussion. (JB)

There is a wind between the worlds, whose existence was undreamed of by scientists – though not by poets – until a dozen years ago. The scientists 'knew' that space was empty, containing nothing but a few stray meteors. Apart from these lonely wanderers, it was a perfect vacuum.

Well, it is not. Almost invariably, the Universe turns out to be more complex than we could have imagined, and this has been true of space. By the time we have finished with it – and it has finished with us – we may well have discovered that the void between the planets is as complicated an environment as the ocean or the atmosphere. Pascal never guessed how far he was from the truth when he expressed terror of the 'silence and emptiness of infinite space'. Infinite it may be, but it is neither silent nor empty, except to our human senses, which have so little contact with reality.

To the radio astronomer, space is full of noises, covering octave after octave of the bands across which he tunes. Though pure noise is all that he has found so far, that has already been enough to transform our knowledge of the Universe. We now know that stars, planets, and galaxies emit characteristic radio waves; we have been able to detect the hiss of these cosmic transmitters out to distances that old-fashioned optical telescopes like the 200-inch reflector on Palomar are powerless to span.

I use the word 'hiss' deliberately, for that is what it sounds like to the ear: raw, undifferentiated noise, identical with that produced by any sensitive radio receiver when it is tuned between stations with the gain control full up. Only at one spot on the cosmic radio band is there a distinctive, sharply tuned signal from space. You will not be able to locate it with your ordinary radio, or even your short-wave set; it is at far too high a frequency (1,420 megacycles, or a wavelength of about eight inches) and also far too feeble. But it is there, and it is one of the most important single keys that the radio astronomers have yet found to the secrets of the Universe.

This 1,420-megacycle signal is not produced by intelligent creatures on other planets. It comes from every part of the sky, and is the song of the hydrogen atoms that drift between the stars. We now believe that most of the matter in the Universe – perhaps more than 90 per cent of it – is hydrogen. Much of it is concentrated into the stars, whose furnaces it fuels; but much more is dispersed among them in a gas billions upon billions of times more tenuous than the air we breathe.

In our corner of the Universe, the Sun itself is the main source of this gas, which it ejects in great clouds that go scudding across the orbits of the planets. Though conclusive proof of this (as of so much else) was not obtained until the International Geophysical Year satellites started circling the Earth, one piece of evidence had pointed to the existence of such hydrogen gales, or 'solar winds', for many years.

Unlike the evidence for most scientific theories, this is visible for all the world to see; it is written across the face of the sky by the tails of comets. Even those who have never seen a comet (and there have been no really spectacular ones during the twentieth century) are familiar with the appearance of these strange visitors, so well described by their ancient name of 'hairy stars'.

Most people, however, are probably under the impression that the tail of a comet streams behind it, like the smoke from an old-time locomotive. This is not so; indeed, the tail is more likely to point *ahead* of the comet, resembling the locomotive's searchlight rather than its smoke trail. The general rule is that, as a comet swings around the Sun – which it may sometimes do on a very tight, hairpin bend – its tail always points away from the Sun, whichever direction the comet itself may be moving. Thus though the tail may stream behind when the comet is making its approach to the Sun, for most of the time it is broadside on to the comet's orbit, or even pointing ahead of it.

There is only one possible explanation for this odd behaviour. Something emanating from the Sun must be sweeping the comet's tail outwards, as the wind carries away the smoke from a chimney stack. In most old astronomy books (and any astronomy book printed more than ten years ago is an old one) you will find it stated with considerable assurance that the pressure of sunlight is the agent responsible.

It is rather hard to realize that sunlight can exert pressure, for what could be more insubstantial than light? But as everyone is well aware since Hiroshima, energy and mass are two sides of the same coin. Light, therefore, has mass and hence momentum; if you hold out your palms towards the sun on a bright clear day the weight of light falling upon them will be about a millionth of an ounce.

It seemed reasonable to assume that out in space this force, weak though it is, might be enough to affect the extremely thin gas composing a comet's tail. However, calculations show that though sunlight may have some minor influence, its pressure is much too feeble to produce the spectacular changes often observed in comets. Occasionally the tail of a comet is torn off by a blast of invisible energy which must be hundreds of times more powerful than mere sunlight. We have, therefore, to look for another explanation, and we find it in the fact that the Sun emits other things besides light. It is the solar wind which carves and shapes the tails of comets.

This wind is electrified, as is all the matter in so intensely hot an object as the Sun. The hydrogen atoms have been torn asunder, and their two components – the central positive proton and its orbiting negative electron – set moving so violently that they cannot recombine. They are like partners who have broken up a sedate waltz and gone spinning off independently in a wild bacchanal.

Such a gas, because it contains equal numbers of positive and negative charges, is itself electrically neutral. It is known as a plasma – a term you will be hearing more and more often in the future, for it represents a state of matter which is becoming of increasing technical importance. You have a sample in your own home, if you employ fluorescent light tubes.

This plasma wind varies with the activity of the Sun in a manner which as yet we cannot begin to predict, or even to explain. We know, however, that it originates from the most violent of all the spectacular events that take place on the Sun's surface – solar flares.

A flare is a sudden local brightening of the Sun's face – usually in the neighbourhood of a sunspot – which may within minutes spread over hundreds of millions of square miles. It lasts from thirty minutes to a few hours; during this short period of time, an area equal to that of a hundred Earths may blaze forth with such brilliance that it outshines even the surrounding incandescence. The energy released by a flare is beyond all imagination, sometimes equalling that of a million H-bombs, and it is not surprising that such explosions blast planet-sized clouds of the Sun's atmosphere into space.

These clouds reach the Earth about a day after they are ejected from the Sun, and their arrival triggers a very complex train of events. Most of that complexity is due to the fact that the Earth possesses a magnetic field which acts like a giant trap, thousands of miles across. Just as iron filings are attracted to the poles of a magnet, so the plasma clouds from the Sun are funnelled down towards the magnetic poles of Earth. When, as often happens, they eventually enter the atmosphere, they make it glow with the wonderful auroral hues that have amazed and baffled men for centuries. Thus even in the depths of the polar night, the colours flickering over the landscape still have their origin in the hidden Sun.

At this point, it may be as well to give some more of the evidence in support of these statements. Much of it is highly technical, but two recent experiments have given direct and dramatic proof that plasma winds do in fact blow from Sun to Earth.

The first involved Pioneer 5, the deep-space probe launched on 11 March 1960 into an orbit towards Venus. Pioneer 5 was tracked out to a distance of 22 million miles, and was the first man-made object ever to send back information from the deeps of interplanetary space. It is still orbiting, its radio voice now silent, between Earth and Venus; perhaps in the far future it may be recovered and displayed in some museum of astronautics as a quaint relic from the past.

Twenty days after launching, when it was three million miles sunward of Earth, Pioneer 5 ran into a great cloud of electrified gas. A little later, that cloud reached Earth, where it was noted by satellites just outside the atmosphere, as well as by instruments at ground level. In a few years, there will undoubtedly be space probes on permanent patrol inside Earth's orbit, to give warning of plasma clouds heading in our direction; as we will see later, such information will one day be literally a matter of life and death. Even now it would be of great value to the radio and cable companies, for these clouds can cause communication blackouts all over the world.

The other evidence comes from Echo 1, the most brilliant of all the satellites, which millions of people saw as a brightly moving star. Echo 1, a hundred feet in diameter, is merely an inflated balloon and so has extremely small mass for its size. Like a drifting soap bubble, it responds to the slightest influences. In fact, it is so flimsy a structure that even the feeble pressure of sunlight has had a very substantial effect on its orbit, changing its distance from Earth by hundreds of miles.

This light-pressure effect is a steady push that builds up uniformly day after day. Occasionally, however, Echo 1 has been buffeted by sudden disturbances which produce sharp changes in its orbit – changes far greater than could be caused by the gentle push of light. These are due to the impact of solar plasmas; though earlier satellites showed similar effects, Echo 1 is the first to be blown badly off course by the winds of space. It will not be the last.

All this may have given you a false idea of the actual strength of the solar wind, so let us compare it with the phenomena of everyday life. It is rather difficult to do so, because the forces and quantities concerned are so far outside the range of ordinary experience that the figures tend to be meaningless: for example, even in the most violent hurricane, wind velocities seldom exceed a hundred miles an hour.

The winds of space blow a little faster, since they can cross the 93 million miles between Sun and Earth in about a day. This gives an average speed of four million miles an hour, but they can probably exceed this on occasion.

Obviously, if the solar wind had a density even remotely approaching that of terrestrial air, it would not merely blow an Echo satellite off course; it would blow Earth out of its orbit, and the whole Solar System would rapidly come apart. Luckily, even the densest plasma cloud from the Sun is so incredibly tenuous that it contains only about two million hydrogen atoms in a volume the size of a matchbox.

Perhaps you think that this is a respectable number, but in a matchboxful of ordinary air, there are not two million but *two thousand million million* million atoms. Or, to put it in a way which is perhaps a little more meaningful, you would have to let a matchbox full of air expand until it was a cube two miles each side before its density had dropped to that of the solar plasma. And this is a peak value, met only when the Sun is active; the normal density is a hundred times smaller than this. It is not surprising, therefore, that the forces produced are extremely small; when you are walking into a gentle breeze, you are fighting a million times the pressure that a man in a space suit would experience if he tried to buck the fiercest wind that blows from the Sun.

Yet feeble though they are, those winds can be deadly and now we come to what may well be their greatest importance in the future. They are responsible for at least one of the huge radiation belts that surround the Earth, which would-be astronauts are now regarding with some alarm.

When it is trapped in the Earth's magnetic field, the solar plasma forms a gigantic doughnut-shaped cloud, the outer Van Allen belt. (The smaller inner belt has a different origin, which does not concern us here.) The discovery of this radiation zone was one of the first, as well as one of the most remarkable, results of the International Geophysical Year. It is hard to realize that to a being who could see by radio waves, our planet would appear surrounded by structures more complex than the rings of Saturn. Yet to our eyes, they are completely invisible, and until the first American satellites started to probe them, scientists had no knowledge of their existence.

These vast smoke rings of electrified gas girdling the world high above the Equator are little danger to outward-bound space travellers, who will flash through them in minutes, but it will be a different matter for man-carrying satellites. The weight of shielding required to protect the crews may make manned space stations impractical in the denser layers of the Van Allen belts. We may have to employ robots here, putting our human observers at higher or lower levels, in the gaps between the radiation zones.

There is, however, one other possibility. If the Van Allen belts prove to be a nuisance, *we may remove them*. This startling (indeed at first sight almost megalomaniac) idea was first put forward by the physicist Professor Fred Singer, who pointed out that as the total amount of material in the belts is extremely small, it would be theoretically possible to neutralize it. This might be done by suitably designed satellites which, after a few hundred or thousand orbits, would sweep up the unwanted particles and make the immediate vicinity of the Earth more fit for human occupation. After air conditioning, space conditioning . . .

That this idea is no fantasy was demonstrated in the summer of 1958, when the Advanced Research Projects Agency of the US Department of Defense conducted what has been, with some justice, called the biggest scientific experiment in history. This experiment – Project Argus – involved not the neutralization of the Earth's radiation belts, but something still more remarkable: *their creation*.

The philosophy behind Project Argus was as follows: if the Sun could produce radiation belts around the Earth by blowing charged particles into the upper atmosphere from space, we should be able to do the same thing by injecting them from beneath. Calculations revealed the surprising fact that even a very small atomic bomb could provide enough plasma to give observable effects.

This suggestion, incidentally, was first made by a rather remarkable man, a Greek electrical engineer named Nicholas Christofilos, who some years ago caused considerable embarrassment to US physicists by suggesting a way in which several million dollars might be saved in the building of their giant accelerators or atom smashers. Because it was couched in somewhat unorthodox mathematics, his letter went into the 'Nuts' file. Here it remained until the principle put forward by Christofilos was independently discovered and announced, and a modest cough from the author drew attention to his priority. This is the sort of incident that can lead to recriminations and lawsuits, but in this case there was a happy ending: Christofilos, despite his lack of the right academic qualifications, was imported into the United States and is now at the University of California's famous Radiation Laboratory.

Project Argus was carried out in great secrecy, as it had profound defence and political implications. On three days in August and September 1958, very small nuclear devices were launched to a height of three hundred miles over the South Atlantic by a US Navy task force, and injected huge numbers of electrons into the upper atmosphere.

Within seconds, the results were noted by ground radar stations, satellites and instrument-carrying rockets in many parts of the globe. Still more impressive is the fact that they were also observed by the naked eye. The August explosions produced spectacular auroral displays, both in the detonation area and thousands of miles away, where the Earth's magnetic field focused the electrons back into the atmosphere. *For the first time, men had made an artificial aurora.*

The plasma from the explosions lasted for many days; indeed, satellite-borne instruments were able to detect some of the Argus electrons three months after they had been shot into orbit. The experiment showed, beyond all doubt, that we now have the power to produce really striking changes in the character of nearby space. Only the future will show what use we make of these powers; a couple of years before Project Argus, in a short story ominously entitled 'Watch This Space', I drew attention to the ghastly possibilities of cosmic advertising, and I only hope that Madison Avenue does not lure Mr Christofilos away from the Radiation Lab.

The Argus experiment was important because of the information it gave about the natural radiation in space; once you can reproduce a phenomenon, you are well on the way to understanding it. Such understanding will be vital when men start to travel between the planets, for not only Earth, but possibly all the major bodies in the Solar System, may have radiation belts. Indeed, there is already some evidence that Jupiter possesses a radiation zone thousands of times more intense than Earth's. We will have to chart these regions and, if necessary, minimize their danger by racing through them at high speed.

The planetary radiation belts probably wax and wane with solar activity, which rises to a peak every eleven years. The Sun was at its maximum in 1958, when the Van Allen zone was discovered, and flares were occurring on its surface at least once a month. Now it is sinking into quiescence, but it will revive again around 1969.

And this is an alarming thought, for just about then manned space flight will be really getting under way. When men start to sail away from the Earth, they will be doing so under the worst possible conditions – into the teeth of the storms of space. The indications are that no practical weight of shielding could protect the crews of a spaceship from a really severe blast of solar plasma. They would feel nothing and see nothing as that impalpable wind swept past their vessel, yet in a few hours they would start to die of radiation poisoning.

What is the answer? It is much too early to be sure. If worst comes to the worst, we will have to travel only when the Sun is quiet. When it is spewing forth its deadly clouds, our ships must remain behind the shield of the Earth's atmosphere, protected as if by a break-water from the gales of space. Since a careful watch on the Sun for solar flares will always give us a day's warning of an approaching storm, this will be no great handicap for lunar travel, for flights to the Moon will last no longer than this.

For ships in deep space, weeks or months away from Earth, it will be a different matter. They could not run for shelter – there might be none within ten million miles – but would have to ride out the storm. Though it would be impossible to provide shielding for an entire ship, the individual crew members might be supplied with thick-walled capsules or storm cellars within which they could remain, cramped but safe, until the danger was past. Eventually, there can be little doubt, we will find ways of deflecting solar plasmas by magnetic or electric fields. The energy required to do so would be very small, though its application is beyond our present-day technologies.

There are many analogies between the seas of Earth and the vaster seas of space; here is a final one. Two centuries ago, when men set out on long ocean voyages, they were attacked by an obscure and horrible disease which often wiped out entire ships' companies. Perhaps radiation sickness will be the scurvy of the first astronauts; its cure, however, will demand more than a few limes and lemons. But we will find it, sooner or later, so that we can safely ride the winds of space.

How strange it is to think that, since the beginning of time, these invisible winds have been sweeping past our world, gusting from Earth to Moon in fifteen minutes, yet until a moment ago, no man dreamed of their existence. What other surprises are waiting for us, out there in what we once believed was empty space?

— 12 —

Space Facts and Space Fallacies

The Chancellor's Address at the University of Moratuwa Convocation, Bandaranaike Memorial International Conference Hall, Colombo, 31 March 1983.

It is now more than fifty years since I started thinking seriously about space travel, and in that time I have seen it go through the three phases characteristic of any new and revolutionary idea. They can be summed up by this set of quotations:

1. 'It's crazy – don't waste my time.'
2. 'It's possible – but not worth doing.'
3. '*I said* it was a good idea, all along.'

The speed with which distinguished scientists can sometimes proceed from Stage 1 to Stage 3 never ceases to amaze me. However, let us not be too critical. So many ideas that sound crazy are indeed crazy, and if a busy man paid equal attention to all of them he would never get anything done. The test of a truly first-rate mind is its readiness to correct mistakes and even to change course completely when the facts merit it.

One of the best examples I can give of this is based on my own experience, and I feel free to pass it on to you as the scientist concerned has been dead for many years.

In 1953 – four years before the launching of the first Earth satellite, Sputnik 1 – New York's Hayden Planetarium asked me to arrange a symposium on space flight. Among the experts I invited was the chief scientist of the US Weather Bureau: I wrote to him asking if he would give us a talk about the possible value of artificial satellites to meteorology. I was flabbergasted by his answer: satellites wouldn't be any use for weather research or forecasting . . .

When the initial shock had worn off, I returned to the attack. I pointed out that we space cadets had been saying for years that satellites *would* be useful to meteorologists; if we were talking nonsense, it was his duty – as one of the leaders in the field – to explain exactly why we were wrong.

To his great credit, the scientist accepted my challenge and started to look into the subject. In the course of writing his paper, he converted himself from a sceptic to a wild enthusiast. A few years later, he was directing the US meteorological satellite programme, and ran it until his untimely death.

This is not a bad example of the way one should treat a new and revolutionary idea. Be sceptical at first, but if it has possibilities – look into it carefully. And if it is *really* valuable – adopt it enthusiastically.

Unfortunately, few people have the mental flexibility needed to do this. This is particularly true when they have, after long study and effort, become 'experts' on some particular subject. Beware of experts, even though they are right 99 per cent of the time – or they wouldn't stay in business. But that remaining 1 per cent, when they are quite wrong, may be what really matters.

I tried to sum this up in what is now fairly well known as Clarke's First Law, viz: 'When a distinguished but elderly scientist says that something is possible, he is almost certainly right. When he says it is impossible, he is very probably wrong.'*

The history of space flight is full of such examples, and in a moment I look forward to giving some choice specimens of ignorance and stupidity I've encountered both at the expert and non-expert levels. But some of the best I've discovered only recently, because the full story could not emerge until war-time security had lapsed – and the principal culprits were safely dead.

The ancestor of today's giant rockets was the German V2 (or A4) designed by Dr Wernher von Braun's team at Peenemünde, and test-flown successfully for the first time on 3 October 1942. With a take-off weight of twelve tons and a range of two hundred miles, it was far in advance of anything else that existed at the time; so much so, in fact, that many of Prime Minister Churchill's wartime advisers

*I would now like to amend this: 'he or she' . . .

refused to believe in its existence. Now that our rockets can go round the world in ninety minutes, and have travelled thousands of millions of miles into outer space, it's hard to realize that only forty years ago distinguished scientists were arguing that a two-hundred-mile range was impossible. And the head of the most famous British fireworks firm stated categorically: 'My family has been making rockets for more than a century. I can assure you that no rocket will ever cross the English Channel.'

The whole story – which would be funny if its implications had not been so tragic – will be found in Professor R. V. Jones' history of British scientific intelligence (or lack of it) during the 1939–45 period, *Most Secret War* (1978). To quote from Jones:

The *naïveté* of our 'experts' was incredible. They were all eminent, some very eminent, in particular fields of science or technology, and yet they were completely out of their depth when dealing with the rocket. I can remember a Fellow of the Royal Society . . . saying that he was amazed at the accuracy with which the Germans would have to set the rocket before launching it . . . What he had calculated, quite possibly correctly, was the trajectory of a rocket fired, as on 5 November, with a stick attached, and launched in the familiar way from a bottle . . . We knew that the Germans were using gyroscopic control, with information . . . transmitted to rudders in the main jet . . . as we explained the system, our scientist looked heavenwards and said, 'Ah, yes, gyroscopes! I hadn't thought of them!' And that was about the level of the better contributions from the experts.

It seems equally incredible that one of the reasons the 'experts' – led by Churchill's chief scientific adviser, Lord Cherwell (Professor Lindemann) – refused to believe in long-range rockets was that they thought only in terms of such solid propellants as cordite. Yet liquid fuels had been known and tested for years, particularly by Robert Goddard in the United States, and almost all the literature of space flight was devoted to them. Despite this, it took months to convince the 'experts' that liquid fuels might make long-range rockets possible. To quote Jones again: 'I can remember at one meeting Sir Robert Robinson saying, "Ah, yes, liquid fuel!" and several others taking up the chorus as though the realization that the fuel could be liquid instead of solid completely exonerated them from their previous failure.' It was the gyroscope story again . . .

But at least even these pathetic 'experts' were not ignorant of one basic fact about rockets – that, unlike all other prime movers, they could operate in the airless vacuum of space. How many times, in the 1930s, we would-be astronauts heard the argument that 'the rocket won't work in a vacuum, because there's nothing for the exhaust to push against'.

Even in those days, it was hard to stomach the sheer Olympian conceit of the critics who brought forward this argument. Apparently they believed that *they* were the very first to wonder if a rocket could work in a vacuum – even though scientists had been thinking about space flight for several generations.

Fallacies are always amusing and are often extremely instructive, for it is by exposing them that one can get a better understanding of the facts that they conceal. One argument that used to be employed against space flight by professional pessimists about fifty years ago ran something like this: 'It takes twenty million foot-pounds of energy to lift one pound out of the Earth's gravitational field. The most powerful propellant combination contains only a quarter of this – five million foot-pounds of energy per pound. Therefore no propellant can even lift itself, let alone anything else, out of the Earth's gravitational field. Therefore space flight is impossible. QED.'

It is surprising how a few figures, quoted with a show of authority, can 'prove' a case. (There is no need for the figures to be right as long as there is no one around who can contradict them.) In the example above, the figures were correct – at least approximately – but the interpretation was hopelessly wrong.

The propellants a rocket carries obviously do not have to lift themselves out of the Earth's gravitational field. If they are burned while the rocket is still close to the Earth – say just above the atmosphere – they impart nearly all their energy to the vehicle and waste little of it lifting their own mass against gravity.

The most extraordinary suggestion I have ever seen concerning rockets, however, was made in perfect seriousness in an old astronautical journal by a gentleman for whom Sir Isaac Newton had obviously lived in vain. He proposed catching the exhaust gases, by means of a funnel behind the rocket motor, and using them over again. This scheme reminds me irresistibly of those cartoons of becalmed yachtsmen blowing furiously at their limp sails with a pair of bellows, and forgetting the unfortunate equality of action and reaction.

A rather more sophisticated piece of spurious reasoning appeared about forty years ago in, I am sorry to say, the leading physics journal of a country not very far from here. The author put forward the curious argument that it is impossible for a body to exceed the velocity of sound in the material of which it is made. As the velocity of escape from the Earth is seven miles a second, and the velocity of sound in most metals barely half that, we would never be able to build rockets that could leave the Earth . . .

It is not surprising that some of the most interesting space fallacies have involved gravity. We will not discuss here the whole range of fictional 'anti-gravity' devices, many of which have their own built-in contradictions, but will concern ourselves with some proposals which at first sight seem quite sound and reasonable.

One of the first involves the question of jumping on a planet of low gravity, such as the Moon. On Earth, the record for the high jump is about seven and a half feet. So at first sight it would seem that on the Moon, where gravity is a one-sixth of Earth's, an Olympic champion should be able to clear a bar at $6 \times 7\frac{1}{2}$ feet, or an impressive 45 feet.

This isn't true, for a number of reasons. First of all, when a man jumps $7\frac{1}{2}$ feet on Earth, he's already starting with his centre of gravity about $3\frac{1}{2}$ feet from the ground – so he's only lifting it an extra 4 feet or so. Assuming that he could put forth the same effort on the Moon, therefore, he could lift his centre of gravity about 24 feet. So the lunar high-jump record couldn't possibly be more than about 27 feet – still impressive, but a long way from 45.

And I doubt if it would be anything like this, even inside a pressurized dome where the athlete was not encumbered with a space suit. It is very difficult to run on the Moon – or even walk naturally – so I'm not sure what sort of take-off speed could be attained.

Many years ago I read a science-fiction serial in which one of the characters jumped off Phobos, the inner moon of Mars, and was in danger of falling on to the planet below. This involves a fallacy to which I'll return later, and it can be said at once that Phobos (diameter about fifteen miles) is too large a body to permit human beings to escape by muscle-power alone. However, there is no doubt that a man could jump off some of the smaller asteroids. The limiting diameter, for one made of ordinary rock, is about four miles, and this raises interesting possibilities for future athletic contests. Interplanetary high-jumping, however, would be almost as boring to watch as cricket,* since it would be many hours before the slowly rising contestants had sorted themselves out into those who had achieved escape velocity, and those who were falling back again . . .

If anyone did succeed in jumping off Phobos – even if he jumped directly towards Mars – there would be no possibility whatsoever of his falling on to the planet, as he would still possess the satellite's orbital velocity, which is almost five thousand miles an hour. All that his jump would have done would be to compound this speed with the very few miles an hour which his own muscles could provide. His velocity vector would therefore be virtually un-changed, and he would still be a satellite of Mars, moving in an orbit very slightly different from that of Phobos. At the most, he would recede a few miles from Phobos – and if he waited three hours and fifty minutes (half a revolution) the two orbits would intersect again and he would return to the surface of the little moon!

Many years ago I wrote a story based on this idea – 'Jupiter V', published in *Reach for Tomorrow* – and I refer you to that if you want to know more about high-jumping on small worlds.

A number of writers have fallen into another gravitational trap by proposing that space travellers should use asteroids or comets to give them free rides. Some asteroids, they point out, have passed within a few hundred thousand miles of Earth and then gone on to cut across the orbits of the other planets. Why not hop aboard such a body as it makes its closest approach to Earth, and then jump off at a convenient moment when passing Mars? In this way your spaceship would only have to cover a fraction of the total distance: the asteroid would do all the real work . . .

The fallacy arises, of course, from thinking of an asteroid as a kind of a bus or escalator. Any asteroid whose path took it close to Earth would be moving at a very high speed relative to us, so that a

---

*I couldn't resist this – Sri Lankans are crazy about cricket . . .

spaceship which tried to reach and actually land on it would need to use a great deal of fuel. And once it had matched speed with the asteroid it would follow the asteroid's orbit whether the asteroid was there or not. There are no circumstances, in fact, where making such a rendezvous would have any effect except that of increasing fuel consumption and adding to the hazards of the voyage. Even if there was any advantage in such a scheme, one might have to wait several hundred years before there was a chance for a return trip. No, interplanetary hitchhiking will not work . . .

The commonest of all gravitational fallacies is that enshrined in the words, 'How high must you go before you get beyond the pull of gravity?' In the public mind, the idea of weightlessness is inseparably tied up with escaping from the gravitational field of the Earth. It is extremely hard to explain in understandable language (a) that one can never 'get beyond the pull of gravity' – because it extends to infinity, and (b) that one can be completely weightless while still in a powerful gravitational field – if one is in free fall.

Perhaps the most complete misunderstanding of conditions in space I have ever encountered was shown by a cartoon-strip artist who depicted two spaceships being coupled together by suction pads. Presumably he had grown a little tired of magnets, and had tried to think of something original.

Though this is not a fallacy in the sense that it can be easily disproved by logic, it seems fairly certain that the fate which would befall the human body when exposed to the vacuum of space has been greatly exaggerated. Certainly there is no question of the body being severely damaged – or even exploding, as some writers have gruesomely imagined. Men have been safely subjected, in explosive decompression tests, to greater pressure changes than would be experienced in a spaceship whose cabin walls were ruptured.

If a man is suddenly plunged into a vacuum, he will of course quickly lose consciousness owing to lack of oxygen. The time quoted for this to happen is about fifteen seconds, but there is little doubt that this could be greatly extended if there was time to make suitable preparations. Divers, by breathing deeply and so flushing out their lungs with air, can hold their breath for three or four minutes. As far as lack of oxygen is concerned, therefore, a man could certainly survive in space for at least a minute.

After a certain length of time, the absence of pressure would cause his blood to vaporize, though at body temperature, so the word 'boiling' is rather misleading. This would be quite a slow process since the veins and arteries are tough enough to provide considerable internal pressure, and the latent heat needed for the boiling process would have to come from somewhere. It seems plausible to assume, therefore, that short excursions into space could be tolerated, at least for emergencies – as Stanley Kubrick showed in *2001: A Space Odyssey*.

Somebody once suggested to me that when a spaceship was under power, the resultant acceleration would cause the air inside the ship to be compressed at one end so that the people 'at the top' might suffocate. Fortunately, this novel danger doesn't bear serious analysis. The atmosphere inside a spaceship under one gravity acceleration would have exactly the same pressure gradient as it would on Earth. I've never heard of anyone suffocating while walking upstairs, though a sufficiently sensitive barometer would show that the pressure in the bedroom is slightly lower than in the kitchen . . .

Designers of the five-mile-long interstellar spaceships launched by the more ambitious science-fiction writers would certainly have to allow for this effect, since the atmospheric pressure difference between the prow and stern of such a vessel would be as great as that between the base and summit of Everest. However, one fancies that this would be among the very least of their problems.

Another astronautical fallacy that still persists is the idea that on the Moon, or in space, the stars are brilliantly visible at all times. Old science-fiction drawings invariably showed lunar landscapes beneath a sky full of stars, with the Sun's corona stretching outwards in a glorious mantle of milky radiance. So, usually, do science-fiction films . . .

The truth is rather different. When a large amount of light enters it, as is normally the case during the daytime, the human eye automatically cuts down its sensitivity. At night, after a period of some minutes, it becomes about a thousand times as sensitive as during the day. It loses that sensitivity at once when it is flooded with light again – as any motorist who has been blinded by an approaching car will testify. During daylight, on the Moon, the eye is constantly picking up the glare from the surrounding landscape. It never has a chance of switching over to its 'high sensitivity' range, and the stars thus remain invisible. Only if the eye is shielded from all other light sources will the stars slowly appear in the jet-black sky.

You can put this to the test quite easily by standing well back from the window in a brilliantly lit room one night, and seeing how many stars you can observe in the sky outside. Then remember that the light reflected from the walls around is only a fraction of the glare that the lunar rocks would throw back.

This situation poses a dilemma to the artist attempting to illustrate lunar scenes. Should he put in the stars or not? After all, they are there and can be seen if you look for them in the right way. Besides, everyone expects to see them in the picture . . . I am afraid one has to cheat and put them in – as indeed Kubrick and I did in *2001*. The same argument applies to the beautiful solar corona: it is impossible to look anywhere near the Sun without dark glasses, so although the corona is there you can't see it, unless you contrive an artificial eclipse and block out the Sun's light completely.

For quite different reasons, the human eye will never see many of the gorgeous colours shown in the magnificent photographs of spiral and gaseous nebulae produced by today's great telescopes. The colours are real enough, but they are so faint that it takes minutes – or hours – of exposure to reveal them. They are below the threshold of vision, just as the colours of our familiar world are under even the brightest of full moons.

I would like to end by discussing what is not only the most fascinating, but also the most important, of all the facts – or fallacies – about space. And this is the existence of extraterrestrial intelligence.

There was a time when we believed that we were alone in the Universe – apart, perhaps, for the not-insignificant exception of God. Then the planets were discovered to be other worlds, and imagination quickly peopled them with inhabitants. From about the seventeenth century onwards, the concept of the 'Plurality of Worlds' has been taken almost for granted. So has the idea that, out there in this immense cosmos of billions upon billions of stars, there *must* be races much superior to mankind.

The invention of the space rocket, and still more the radio telescope, added a new dimension to this argument. For the first time there was a means – in theory at least – of discovering extra-terrestrial intelligence, and perhaps communicating with it. No wonder that there is now great public interest in SETI and the even more ambitious CETI (Search for and Contact with Extra-Terrestrial Intelligence). Undoubtedly Carl Sagan's splendid *Cosmos* television series and such movies as *E. T.* and *Close Encounters of the Third Kind* have been largely responsible for this state of affairs, though unfortunately they have also spawned such pathological by-products as flying saucer cults.

Now there has been a reaction – a scientific backlash. Because our very limited investigations over a mere few decades have produced not the slightest hard evidence for the existence of extraterrestrials, some scientists have gone to the other extreme. They argue that intelligent life outside this planet may be so exceedingly rare that we will never be able to discover its existence. Some have even suggested that we may be unique – the only intelligence in the whole of Creation!

This point of view has been put most forcibly by the American mathematical physicist Dr Frank Tipler. One of his most interesting arguments runs something like this:

We have started to build robot space explorers, and in the very near future – after a century or so at the most – will be able to make far more sophisticated ones which, when they reach new planets, *can reproduce themselves from local materials*. Such 'von Neumann machines', as the class of self-replicating automata is called, would obey the old biblical command 'be fruitful and multiply', in a kind of cosmic chain reaction, until they had filled the Galaxy.

This would take only a few millions of years, and the Galaxy is a thousand times older. So it should have happened long ago – *if* there ever were intelligent and inquisitive creatures out among the stars. But it hasn't . . . At least, we don't think it has. Therefore, ours must be the first technological civilization to make its appearance in this Galaxy, and perhaps in the whole of space.

Of course, Tipler's argument is considerably more sophisticated than this, and I haven't done it justice. One can think of many possible refutations – and people like Carl Sagan are busily doing just that. It has now become almost a theological issue, and the tantalizing thing is that if Tipler is right, we'll never know. It would be possible to prove that extraterrestrials exist by meeting them; it won't be possible to prove that they don't exist – without exploring the whole of space and time. For, as has been wittily said: 'Absence of evidence if not evidence of absence.'

So – what is fact, and what is fallacy, in this most fascinating, and most portentous of all cosmological debates? *Do we have neighbours?*

We may never know . . .

We may get an answer a thousand years from now . . . Or it may be the only headline in tomorrow's newspapers.

— 13 —

When the Aliens Come

Where would science fiction be without the BEM (Bug-Eyed Monster)? I have (usually) avoided them in my own writings, but have a sneaking fondness for them. Here is my attempt to put the record straight in Playboy *magazine, January 1968.*

The first encounter between Earthman and Alien is one of the oldest and most hackneyed themes of science fiction. Indeed, it has now become such a cliché that 'take me to your leader' jokes are perfectly familiar even to those benighted souls who have never read a word of science fiction in their lives.

How odd, therefore, that there seem to be so few serious *factual* discussions of this subject. True, there have been essays without number on the possibilities of extraterrestrial life and the ways we might communicate with it, but most of them stop abruptly at the really interesting point. The astronomers and biologists, and even the philosophers and theologians, have all had their say in the last few years. But the sociologists and politicians have left it to the science-fiction writers – and this at the very time when the subject is moving out of the realm of fantasy.

All War Departments, it is said (though one sometimes doubts this), have plans worked out for every conceivable eventuality. Presumably somewhere in the Pentagon are the orders for such lamentable necessities as the invasion of Canada or the bombing of London – or even New York, *vide Fail Safe*. If there are any plans for the defence of Earth, no one has ever mentioned them.

Probably the US Department of Defense would argue, if pressed, that the matter was under the jurisdiction of the State Department – and you may be quite surprised to learn that State *does* have an 'Office of Outer Space Affairs'. On 15 March 1967, its director Robert F. Packard presented a paper on 'The Role of the Diplomat' to the Fifth Goddard Memorial Symposium in Washington. It was concerned, however, exclusively with terrestrial diplomats and did not even hint that there might be any other kind. In the absence of any official guidance, therefore, let us attempt to construct some scenarios (I believe this is the approved term among the nuclear Doomsday planners) of our own.

The first problem we have to face is our total ignorance of the nature of extraterrestrials (ETs) – we do not even know if they exist! If they don't, of course, that is the end of the matter – but even if this is true, *we can never be sure.* And the idea that we are the only intelligent creatures in a Cosmos of a hundred million galaxies is so preposterous that there are very few astronomers today who would take it seriously.

It is safest to assume, therefore, that They *are* out there and to consider the manner in which this fact may impinge upon human society. It could come in ways as undramatic as the deciphering of an ancient papyrus, or as shattering as a crash landing, with ray guns ablaze, on the White House lawn.

The most probable scenario, at least during the foreseeable future, might be called 'Discovery Without Contact'. By this I mean that we obtain unequivocal proof that intelligent ETs exist (or have existed), but in a manner that excludes communication.

Such a proof might be obtained from archaeology or geology. The discovery of a fossilized transistor radio in an undisturbed coal bed, preferably accompanied by skeletons that did not fit into any evolutionary tree, would be convincing evidence that our planet was once visited from space. Ancient legends, wall paintings, or other works of art might also record such visits in historic times; unfortunately, this type of evidence can only be circumstantial – it can never be conclusive.

Shklovskii and Sagan's fascinating book *Inteligent Life in the Universe* reproduces some three-thousand-year-old Babylonian seals which, together with their associated legends, can very easily be taken to depict encounters between men and non-men; parts of the Bible have been interpreted in the same manner. However, the myth-making abilities of the human mind are so unlimited that it would be very foolish to accept these items as proof of anything. After all, what would intelligent aliens make of a Superman comic strip?

No; in a matter as important as this, the only acceptable evidence would be hardware. Quite some years go, in a short story 'The Sentinel' (which Stanley Kubrick later used as the basis of *2001: A Space Odyssey*), I suggested that the best place to look for such evidence would be on a relatively stable and changeless world like the Moon. On Earth, with its incessant weather and geological upheavals, no extraterrestrial artifact would survive for very long, though this is no excuse for not keeping our eyes open. The reason why space hardware has never been discovered may simply be because no archaeologist ever dreamed of looking for it.

Although the philosophical – and sensational – impact of such a discovery would be enormous, after the initial excitement had ebbed the world would probably continue on its way much as before. Once he had read a few Sunday supplements and watched a few TV specials, the proverbial man in the street would say, 'This is all very interesting, but it happened a long time ago and hasn't anything to do with me. Sure, They could come back one day, but there are plenty of more important things to worry about.' And he would be quite right.

Almost every field of scientific inquiry, however, would be profoundly affected. If it appeared that the visitors came from one of the other worlds of our own Solar System – Mars, for example – this would obviously be a great stimulus to planetary exploration, but it would also start us searching much farther afield.

Two intelligent races in the same Solar System, even if they were separated by millions of years of time, would provide virtually conclusive proof that higher civilizations were very common throughout the Universe. This would immediately stimulate really determined attempts to detect signals from other star systems.

Little more than a decade ago, the astronomers suddenly realized, to their considerable surprise, that our radio technology has advanced to the point where we can start talking seriously about interstellar communication. And if, after only fifty years, we have reached such a level of development, what might older civilizations have achieved?

Scattered among the stars there may be radio beacons and transmitters of unimaginable power; the British cosmologist Fred Hoyle has expressed the view that there may be a kind of galactic communications network, linking thousands or millions of worlds. Within a very few centuries, we may be clever enough to plug ourselves into the circuit; it may take us a little longer to understand what the other subscribers are saying. (Conceivably, 'Get off the line!')

The possibilities opened up even by one-way communication (passive eavesdropping) are almost unlimited. The signals would certainly contain visual material – not necessarily real-time TV – which it would be rather easy to reconstruct. And then, across the light-years, we would be able to *look* at other worlds and other races . . .

Now this is a situation far more exciting than the discovery of fossil artifacts. We would be dealing not with prehistory, but with news – though news that had been slightly delayed in transit. If the signals came from the very closest stars, they would have left their transmitters only five or ten years ago; a more likely time lag would be a few centuries. In any event, we would be listening to civilizations still in existence, not studying the relics of vanished cultures.

The things we could learn might change our own society beyond recognition. It would be as if the America of Lincoln's time could tune into the TV programmes of today; though there would be much that could not be understood, there would also be clues that could leapfrog whole technologies into the future. (Ironically enough, the commercials would contain some of the most valuable information!) Nineteenth-century viewers would see that heavier-than-air machines were possible, and simple observation would reveal the principles of their design. The still unimagined uses of electricity would be demonstrated (the telephone, the electric light . . .), and this would be enough to set scientists on the right track. For knowing that a thing can be done is more than half the battle.

As signals from the stars could be received only by nations possessing very large radio telescopes, there would be the opportunity – and the temptation – to keep them secret. Knowledge is the most precious of all commodities, and it is a strange thought that the balance of power may one day be shifted by a few micromicrowatts collected from the depths of space. Yet it should no longer surprise us; for who dreamed, fifty years ago, that the faint flicker of d atoms in a physics lab would change the course of history?

Glimpses of supercivilizations could have either stimulating or stultifying effects on our society. If the technological gulf was not too great to be bridged, and the programmes we intercepted contained hints and clues that we could understand, we would probably rise to the challenge. But if we found ourselves in the position of Neanderthalers confronted by New York City, the psychological shock could be so great that we might give up the struggle. This appears to have happened on our own world from time to time, when primitive races have come into contact with more advanced ones. We will have a good chance of studying this phenomenon in a very few years, when communications satellites start beaming our TV programmes into such places as the Amazon jungle. This is the last century during which widely disparate cultures will exist on Earth; would-be students of astrosociology should make the most of their opportunity before it vanishes for ever. And no one will be surprised to hear that Margaret Mead was intensely interested in space flight . . .

The discovery of an active communications network in our region of space (and I would make a small bet that such a thing exists) would at once raise a very difficult problem: Should we announce our presence by joining in the conversation, or should we maintain a discreet silence? If anyone thinks that this is an easy question to answer, let him put himself in the place of a cultured and sensitive extraterrestrial whose knowledge of human civilization is based largely on 'Dallas', 'L. A. Law' and 'The Late, Late Show'.

Probably everyone would agree that the wisest plan would be to listen carefully until we had learned as much as possible, before attempting to signal our presence. However, such caution may already be much too late; as far as Earth is concerned, the electronic cat was let out of the bag a couple of decades ago. Although it is unlikely that our first radio programmes have ever been monitored (they were too low-powered, and at unfavourable frequencies), the megawatt radars developed during World War II may have been detected tens of light-years away. We have been making such a din that the neighbours can hardly have overlooked us, and I sometimes wonder when they will start banging on the walls.

Of course, if intelligent civilizations are so far apart that no *physical* transport between them is possible (as most scientists believe), then there would seem no objection to announcing our presence. As the old jingle puts it, 'Sticks and stones can break my bones, but words will never hurt me.' Some writers have argued that we should be thankful for the immense distances of interstellar space. Cosmic communities can talk to one another for their mutual benefit, but they can never do each other any harm.

However, this is a naïve and unrealistic view. Even if star travel is impossible (though we have reasons for believing that, on the contrary, it is rather easy), 'mere' communications could do a lot of damage. After all, this is the basis on which all censors act. A really malevolent society could destroy another one quite effectively by a few items of well-chosen information. ('Now, kiddies, after you've prepared your uranium hexafluoride . . . ')

In any case, after a certain level of technical sophistication it is meaningless to distinguish between the transfer of material objects and the transfer of information. Fred Hoyle, in his novel *A for Andromeda*, has suggested that a sufficiently complex signal from space might serve as the genetic blueprint for constructing an extraterrestrial entity. An invasion by radio may seem a little far-fetched, but it does not involve any scientific impossibilities.

I suspect that once we had heard voices echoing between the stars, it would not be long before curiosity – or egotism – made us join the conversation. However, the task of framing suitable replies might be difficult. Naturally, we would present ourselves in the best possible light, and the temptation to gloss over unflattering aspects of human history and behaviour would be considerable. Also – who would speak for man? It is easy to imagine our current ideologies proclaiming their rival merits to the heavens, and even a supercivilization might well be baffled by propaganda blasts based on the teachings of Chairman Mao.

Perhaps fortunately, the power and the resources needed to beam a profile of *Homo sapiens* across interstellar space are so great that a global, co-operative effort would be needed. Then, for the first time, mankind might speak with a single voice; and the problem of compiling the programme might induce a certain humility.

After that, there would come the long wait for the answer. In the unlikely event that there is a civilization circling the very nearest star – Proxima Centauri – we could not receive a reply in less than eight years. It is more probable that the delay would be measured in decades, so any two-way conversations would be distinctly tedious. They would, in fact, be long-term research projects, with scientists receiving in their old age answers to questions they had asked in their youth.

Despite its unavoidable slowness, such conversation-without-contact would, over the centuries, have enormous and perhaps decisive effects upon human society. Quite apart from the technological leapfrogging already mentioned, it could produce knowledge of different races, patterns of thought and political systems that would completely change our philosophical and religious views. Are good and evil man-made concepts? Do other races have gods, and of what nature? Is death universal? These are a few of the questions we might ask of the stars, and some of the answers might not be to our liking.

Yet perhaps the most important result of such contacts might be the simple proof that other intelligent races do exist. Even if our cosmic conversations never rise above the 'Me Tarzan–You Jane' level, we would no longer feel so alone in an apparently hostile Universe. And, above all, knowledge that other beings had safely passed their nuclear crises would give us renewed hope for our own future. It would help to dispel present nagging doubts about the survival value of intelligence. We have, as yet, no definite proof that too much brain, like too much armour, is not one of those unfortunate evolutionary accidents that leads to the annihilation of its possessors.

If, however, this dangerous gift *can* be turned to advantage, then all over the Universe there must be races that have been gathering knowledge, and perfecting their technologies, for periods of time that may be measured in millions of years. Anything that is theoretically possible, and is worth doing, will have been achieved. Among those achievements will be the crossing of interstellar space.

Travel to the stars requires no more energy and demands no more of propulsion systems than flight to the nearest planets. There are rockets in existence today that could launch tonnage payloads to Proxima Centauri; however, it would take them about a quarter of a million years to get there – and Proxima, remember, is the very closest of our stellar neighbours. We will have to move a little faster.

But even at the speed of light (about twenty thousand times greater than that of any space probe yet built) Proxima is still four years away, and it would take over a hundred thousand years to cross the width of the Galaxy.

Yet this does not prove, as many scientists have rashly argued, that interstellar flight is impossible. There are several ways in which it might be achieved, by technologies which even we can imagine, and which might be within our grasp a few centuries from today.

It is highly probable – though not absolutely certain – that the velocity of light can never be exceeded by any material object. Star travel will thus be very time-consuming; the duration of voyages will be measured in decades at the very least – more likely, in millennia. For such short-lived creatures as human beings, this would require multigeneration trips in totally enclosed, self-contained mobile wordlets (little Earths) – or, perhaps less technically demanding, some form of suspended animation.

There is another factor which is almost invariably overlooked in discussions of star travel. Our understandable doubts about the practicability and desirability of such ventures would not be shared by really advanced creatures, who might have unlimited life spans. If we were immortal, the stars would not seem very far away.

It is, therefore, quite unrealistic not to expect visitors from deep space, sooner or later. And, of course, a great many people – not all of them cranks – think that they are arriving right now.

UFOlogy is a can of worms into which I refuse to probe. Let us take the line of least resistance and assume that the strange apparitions whizzing through our skies are indeed of extraterrestrial origin, and that this is finally proved beyond all reasonable doubt.

The first result would be a drastic lowering of the international temperature; any current wars would rapidly liquidate themselves. This point has been made by numerous writers – starting with André Maurois, whose *War Against the Moon* suggested half a century ago that the only way to secure peace on Earth would be to manufacture a fake menace from space. A genuine one would be even more effective.

If, however, the ETs did nothing but merely study us like detached anthropologists, eventually we would resume our pastimes – including minor wars – though with a certain tendency to keep looking over our shoulders. Anyone who has observed the neat farms on the slopes of a volcano will agree that the human race has an astonishing ability to continue life as if nothing has happened even when something very obviously has. We can be sure, though, that under the cover of normalcy there would be heroic attempts by all the secret services and intelligence agencies to establish contact with the aliens – for the exclusive benefit of their respective countries. Every astronomical observatory in the Free World would be pelted with largesse from the CIA.

Such a situation, though it might endure for a decade or so, could not be stable. Sooner or later there would be a communications breakthrough, or else the human race would become so exasperated by the spectacle of Olympian indifference that an 'Aliens Go Home!' movement would develop. Rude radio noises would eventually escalate to nuclear bombs, at which point the aliens either *would* go home or would take steps to abate the nuisance.

It has often been suggested that the arrival of visitors from space would cause widespread panic; for this reason, some UFO enthusiasts believe that the US government is keeping the 'facts' concealed. (Actually, the reverse is nearer the truth; as one Pentagonian once remarked sourly, 'If there really were flying saucers, all us majors would be colonels.') The world has become much more sophisticated since the far-off days of Orson Welles' famous radio broadcast. It is unlikely that a friendly or neutral contact – except in primitive communities, or by creatures of outrageous appearance – would produce an outburst of hysteria like that which afflicted New Jersey in 1938. Thousands of people would probably rush to their cars, but they would be in a hurry to get to the scene of such a historic event, not to escape from it.

And yet, having written those words, I begin to wonder. It is easy to be calm and collected when discussing a theoretical possibility; in the event, one's behaviour may be very different. Like any reasonably observant person who lives under clear skies, I have seen a good many objects that could have been taken for UFOs, and on just one occasion it seemed as if it might be the 'real thing'. (No one will ever believe this, but I was with Stanley Kubrick, the very night we decided to make our movie.*) I shall never forget the feelings of awe and wonder – yes, and fear – that chased each other through my mind, before I discovered that the object was only Echo 1, seen under somewhat unusual conditions.

No one can be sure how he would react in the presence of a visitor from another world. When the time comes to announce that mankind is no longer alone, those who prepare and issue the statement will have a truly terrifying responsibility. Though they will certainly try to sound reassuring, they will know that they are whistling in the dark.

It is impossible to guess at all the motivations which might drive ETs to visit our planet. Human societies have an almost unbelievable range of behaviour, and totally alien cultures might act in ways quite incomprehensible to us. Anyone who doubts this should attempt to look at our own society from outside, and imagine himself in the role of an intelligent Martian trying to understand what was really going on at a political rally, a chess tournament, the floor of the Stock Exchange, a religious revival, a symphony concert, a baseball game, a sit-in, a TV quiz programme – the list is endless.

In a witty essay on 'Extraterrestrial Linguistics' Professor Solomon Golumb of the University of Southern California has tried to make order out of chaos by suggesting that our neighbours might wish to deal with us under one or another of these headings: (1) Help! (2) Buy! (3) Convert! (4) Vacate! (5) Negotiate! (6) Work! (7) Discuss! And a famous short story of Damon Knight's has added (8) Serve! (boiled or fried).

Yet even this rather comprehensive list assumes that They possess psychologies similar to ours, and that we can make mental or at least physical contact. Some ingenious science-fiction writers have argued that this may not necessarily be the case. In Olaf Stapledon's tremendous history of the future, *Last and First Men*,

*See 'Son of Dr Strangelove', p. 146.

the Earth was invaded by microscopic creatures from Mars who formed a rational entity only when they coalesced into a kind of intelligent cloud. (If this seems far-fetched, consider how many independently viable living cells go to form the entity you are pleased to call You.) Because Stapledon's Martians found it very exhausting to assume the solid state, they worshipped hard, rigid bodies and thus avidly collected diamonds and other gems, while ignoring the soft, semi-liquid creatures who transported these sacred objects. They were aware of cars, but not of human beings . . .

Indeed, it has been suggested that any dispassionate observer of the United States would conclude that the car was its dominant life form.

It would be difficult to bridge such a psychophysical gulf; a similar one may already exist right here on Earth, between man and such social insects as ants, termites or bees. Here the individual is nothing: the state is all, beyond the wildest dreams of any totalitarian dictator.

In extreme cases, we might not even be able to *detect* an alien species, except by rather sophisticated instruments. It could be gaseous, or electronic, or could operate on time scales hundreds of times faster or slower than ours. Even human beings live at different rates, judging by speeds of conversation, and there seems little doubt that dolphins think and speak much more rapidly than we do, though they are courteous enough to use slow-speed baby talk when we attempt to communicate with them.

I mention these rather far-out speculations not because I take them very seriously (I don't) but because they show the utter lack of imagination of those who think that intelligent aliens must be humanoid. Now there may well be millions of intelligent humanoid races in the Universe, since ours appears to be a successful and practical design. But even if all the ingredients are exactly the same, and in approximately the same places, it would be exceedingly rare to find a humanoid alien who resembled a man as closely as does, say, a chimpanzee.

I would even go so far as to say that, from the cosmic viewpoint, all terrestrial mammals are 'humanoid'. They all have four limbs, two eyes, two ears, one mouth, arranged symmetrically about a single axis. Could a visitor from Sirius really tell the difference between a man and, for example, a bear? ('I'm terribly sorry, Mr Prime Minister, but all humanoids look the same to me . . . ')

Even if we restrict ourselves to the sense organs and manipulators with which we are familiar on Earth, they could be arranged – and, equally important, used – in an enormous variety of ways, to produce effects of astonishing strangeness. The late Nobel Laureate Dr Hermann Muller expressed this very well in his phrase, 'the bizarreness of the right and proper'. An alien, he pointed out, 'would find it most remarkable that we had an organ combining the requirements of breathing ingesting, chewing, biting, and on occasion fighting, helping to thread needles, yelling, whistling, lecturing and grimacing. He might well have separate organs for all these purposes, located in diverse parts of his body, and would consider as awkward and primitive our imperfect separation of those functions.'

Even judging by the examples on our own world, where all life is based on the same biochemical system, the ingenuity of nature seems almost unlimited. Consider the nightmare shapes of the deep sea or the armoured gargoyles of the insect world; we may one day encounter rational creatures in forms analogous to all of these. And, conversely, we should not be misled by superficial resemblances; think of the abyss that separates the sharks from their almost-duplicates, the dolphins. Or, nearer home, that which tragically divides the sundered children of Abraham today . . .

So, beyond doubt, physical shape is unimportant compared with motivation. Once again, because of our blinkered human viewpoint, we cannot extend our ideas much beyond Dr Golumb's not altogether facetious list of directives. Now although everything that is conceivable will occur at least once, in our Galaxy of a hundred billion suns, some of these categories seem more likely than others. The insanely malevolent invaders beloved by the horror comics have perhaps the least plausibility – if only because they would have destroyed themselves long before they got to us. Any race intelligent enough to conquer interstellar space must first have conquered its own inner demons.

Moreover, there seem few grounds for cosmic conflict, even if it were technically possible. It is hard to see what attractions our world could offer visitors from space; since their physical forms and requirements would be totally different from ours, it is very unlikely that they would be able to live here.

There are no material objects – no conceivable treasures or spices or jewels or exotic drugs – valuable enough to justify the conquest of a world. Anything we possess, they could manufacture easily enough at home. For imagine what our chemists will have done, a thousand years from now.

There may, of course, be entities who collect solar systems as a child may collect stamps. If this happened to us, we might never be aware of it. What do the inhabitants of a beehive know of their keeper?

That may be an analogy worth pursuing. Men do not interfere with bees – or wasps – unless they have good reasons: as far as possible, they prefer to leave them alone. Though we possess no better weapons than 100-megaton bombs, we are not entirely defenceless, and even an advanced supercivilization might think twice about tangling with us.

If they were desperate – if, for example, they were the last survivors of an ancient race, whose mobile worldlet had almost exhausted its supplies after aeons of voyaging – they might be tempted to make a fresh home in our Solar System. But even in that case, co-operation would be to their advantage – and to ours. Since they would probably be able to transmute any element into any other, there is no reason why they should covet Earth. The barren Moon and the drifting slag heaps of the asteroid belt would provide all the raw materials they needed – and the Sun, all the energy. Our planet intercepts only one part in two billion of the radiation pouring from the Sun, and we actually utilize only a minute fraction of that. There is matter and energy enough in the Solar System for many civilizations, for ages to come.

Unfortunately, our record so far has not shown much inclination for peaceful coexistence. If such writers as Robert Ardrey are correct, much of human (and animal) behaviour is determined by the concept of 'territoriality'. The landowner who places a sign on a piece of private wilderness announcing that 'Trespassers Will Be Prosecuted' would then speak for his entire species. If some inoffensive visitors began to colonize the frozen outer moon of

Jupiter, there would be angry voices proclaiming it sacred soil, and retired generals would warn us to keep our lasers dry, and not to fire until we can see the greens of their eyes.

All of which leads to a conclusion that may not be very original but whose importance cannot be overstressed. Everyone recognizes that our present racial, political, and international troubles are symptoms of a sickness which must be cured before we can survive on our own planet – but the stakes may be even greater than that.

Though it is impossible to guard against all the eventualities that the future may bring, if we can learn to live with ourselves we will at least improve our chances of living with aliens. And that word 'ourselves' should be interpreted in the widest possible context to embrace, as far as practical, all intelligent creatures on this planet. At the moment, in a paroxysm of greed and folly, we have virtually exterminated the largest animal this world has ever seen. Only a few eccentrics have felt any twinges of conscience over the fact that the brain of a blue whale is larger than a man's, so that we do not know what kind of entity we have really destroyed.

It is true that our aggressive instincts, inherited from the predatory apes who were our ancestors, have made us masters of this planet and have already propelled us into space. Without those instincts, we might have perished long ago; they have served us well. But, to quote the ruler of Camelot, 'The old order changeth, giving place to new . . . Lest one good custom should corrupt the world.'

We have the intelligence to change, or at least to control, the atavistic urges programmed into our behaviour. Though it may seem a paradox, and a denial of all past history, gentleness and tolerance may yet prove to have the greatest survival value, when we move out into the cosmic stage.

If this is true, let us hope that we have time to cultivate these virtues. For the hour is very late, and no one can guess how many strange eyes and minds are already turned upon the planet Earth.

— 14 —

Report on Planet Three

*This essay – an attempt to widen the mental horizons of geocentric
readers – was published in* Holiday *magazine in May 1959. Although
somewhat dated by later discoveries on Mars (not least the fact that
there were no Martians around as recently as 4000 BC) its conclusions
are still valid.*

*Earth is not a likely abode of intelligent life forms. See the evening
TV news.*

[The following document, which has just been deciphered for the Interplanetary Archaeological Commission, is one of the most remarkable that
has yet been discovered on Mars, and throws a vivid light upon the scientific
knowledge and mental processes of our vanished neighbours. It dates from
the Late Uranium (i.e., final) Age of the Martian civilization, and thus was
written little more than a thousand years before the birth of Christ.

The translation is believed to be reasonably accurate, though a few
conjectural passages have been indicated. Where necessary, Martian terms
and units have been converted into their terrestrial equivalents for ease of
understanding. TRANSLATOR]

The recent close approach of the planet Earth has once again
revived speculations about the possibility of life upon our nearest
neighbour in space. This is a question which has been debated for
centuries, without conclusive results. In the last few years, however, the development of new astronomical instruments has given
us much more accurate information about the other planets.
Though we cannot yet confirm or deny the existence of terrestrial
life, we now have much more precise knowledge of conditions on
Earth and can base our discussions on a firm scientific foundation.

One of the most tantalizing things about Earth is that we cannot
see it when it is closest, since it is then between us and the Sun and its
dark side is therefore turned towards us. We have to wait until it is a

morning or evening star, and thus a hundred million or more miles away from us, before we can see much of its illuminated surface. In the telescope, it then appears as a brilliant crescent, with its single giant Moon hanging beside it. The contrast in colour between the two bodies is striking; the Moon is a pure silvery-white, but the Earth is a sickly blue-green. [The exact force of the adjective is uncertain; it is definitely unflattering. 'Hideous' and 'virulent' have been suggested as alternatives. TRANSLATOR]

As the Earth turns on its axis – its day is just half an hour shorter than ours – different areas of the planet swing out of darkness and appear on the illuminated crescent. By carrying out observations over a period of weeks, it is possible to construct maps of the entire surface, and these have revealed the astonishing fact that *more than two-thirds of the planet Earth is covered with liquid*.

Despite the violent controversy that has raged over this matter for some centuries, there is no longer any reasonable doubt that this liquid is water. Rare though water now is upon Mars, we have good evidence that in the remote past much of our planet was submerged beneath vast quantities of this peculiar compound; it appears, therefore, that Earth is in a state corresponding to our own world several billion years ago. We have no way of telling how deep the terrestrial 'oceans' – to give them their scientific name – may be, but some astronomers have suggested that they are as much as a thousand feet in thickness.

The planet also has a very much more abundant atmosphere than ours; calculations indicate that it is at least ten times as dense. Until quite recently, we had no way of guessing the composition of that atmosphere, but the spectroscope has now solved this problem – with surprising results. The thick gaseous envelope surrounding the Earth contains large amounts of the poisonous and very reactive element oxygen, of which scarcely a trace exists in our own air. Earth's atmosphere also holds considerable quantities of nitrogen and water vapour, which forms huge clouds, often persisting for many days and obscuring large areas of the planet.

Being some 25 per cent nearer the Sun than Mars, Earth is at a considerably higher temperature than our world. Readings taken by thermocouples attached to our largest telescopes reveal intolerable temperatures on its Equator; at higher latitudes, however, conditions are much less extreme, and the presence of extensive ice-caps at both poles indicates that temperatures there are often quite comfortable. These polar ice-caps never melt completely, as do ours during the summer, so they must be of immense thickness.

As Earth is a much larger planet than Mars (having twice our diameter), its gravity is a good deal more powerful. It is, indeed, no less than three times as great, so that a 170-pound man would weigh a quarter of a ton on Earth. This high gravity must have many important consequences, not all of which we can foresee. It would rule out any large forms of life, since they would be crushed under their own weight. It is something of a paradox, however, that Earth possesses mountains far higher than any that exist on Mars; this is probably another proof that it is a young and primitive planet, whose original surface features have not yet eroded away.

Looking at these well-established facts, we can now weigh the prospects for life on Earth. It must be said at once that they appear extremely poor; however, let us be open-minded and prepared to accept even the most unlikely possibilities, as long as they do not conflict with scientific laws.

The first great objection to terrestrial life – which many experts consider conclusive – is the intensely poisonous atmosphere. The presence of such large quantities of gaseous oxygen poses a major scientific problem, which we are still far from solving. Oxygen is so reactive that it cannot normally exist in the free state; on our own planet, for example, it is combined with iron to form the beautiful red deserts that cover so much of the world. It is the absence of these areas which gives Earth its unpleasant greenish hue.

Some unknown process must be taking place on Earth which liberates immense quantities of this gas. Certain speculative writers have suggested that terrestrial life forms may actually release oxygen during the course of their metabolism. Before we dismiss this idea as being too fanciful, it is worth noting that several primitive and now extinct forms of Martian vegetation did precisely this. Nevertheless, it is very hard to believe that plants of this type can exist on Earth in the inconceivably vast quantities which would be needed to provide so much free oxygen. [We know better, of course. All the Earth's oxygen is a by-product of vegetation; our

planet's original atmosphere, like that of Mars today, was oxygen-free.
TRANSLATOR]

Even if we assume that creatures exist on Earth which can survive in so poisonous and chemically reactive an atmosphere, the presence of these immense amounts of oxygen has two other effects. The first is rather subtle, and has only recently been discovered by a brilliant piece of theoretical research, now fully confirmed by observations.

It appears that at a great altitude in the Earth's atmosphere – some twenty or thirty miles – the oxygen forms a gas known as ozone, containing three atoms of oxygen as compared with the normal molecule's two. This gas, though it exists in very small quantities so far from the ground, has an overwhelmingly important effect upon terrestrial conditions. It almost completely blocks the ultraviolet rays of the Sun, preventing them from reaching the surface of the planet.

This fact alone would make it impossible for the life forms we know to exist on Earth. The Sun's ultraviolet radiation, which reaches the surface of Mars almost unhindered, is essential to our well-being and provides our bodies with much of their energy. Even if we could withstand the corrosive atmosphere of Earth, we should soon perish because of this lack of vital radiation.

The second result of the high oxygen concentration is even more catastrophic. It involves a terrifying phenomenon, fortunately known only in the laboratory, which scientists have christened 'fire'.

Many ordinary substances, when immersed in an atmosphere like that of Earth's and heated to quite modest temperatures, begin a violent and continuous chemical reaction which does not cease until they are completely consumed. During the process, intolerable quantities of heat and light are generated, together with clouds of noxious gases. Those who have witnessed this phenomenon under controlled laboratory conditions describe it as quite awe-inspiring; it is certainly fortunate for us that it can never occur on Mars.

Yet it must be quite common on Earth – and no possible forms of life could exist in its presence. Observations of the night side of Earth have often revealed bright glowing areas where fire is raging; though some students of the planet have tried, optimistically, to explain these glows as the lights of cities, this theory must be rejected. The glowing regions are much too variable; with few exceptions, they are quite short-lived, and they are not fixed in location. [These observations were doubtless due to forest fires and volcanoes – the latter unknown on Mars. It is a tragic irony of fate that had the Martian astronomers survived a few more thousand years, they would have seen the lights of man's cities. We missed each other in time by less than a millionth of the age of our planets. TRANSLATOR]

Its dense, moisture-laden atmosphere, high gravity and closeness to the Sun make Earth a world of violent climatic extremes. Storms of unimaginable intensity have been observed raging over vast areas of the planet, some of them accompanied by spectacular electrical disturbances, easily detected by sensitive radio receivers here on Mars. It is hard to believe that any form of life could withstand these natural convulsions, from which the planet is seldom completely free.

Although the range of temperatures between the terrestrial winter and summer is not so great as on our world, this is slight compensation for other handicaps. On Mars, all mobile life forms can easily escape the winter by migration. There are no mountains or seas to bar the way; the small size of our world – as compared with Earth – and the greater length of the year make such seasonable movements a simple matter, requiring an average speed of only some ten miles a day. There is no need for us to endure the winter, and few Martian creatures do so.

It must be quite otherwise on Earth. The sheer size of the planet, coupled with the shortness of the year (which only lasts about six of our months) means that any terrestrial beings would have to migrate at a speed of about fifty miles a day in order to escape from the rigours of winter. Even if such a rate could be achieved (and the powerful gravity makes this appear most unlikely), mountains and oceans would create insuperable barriers.

Some writers of science fiction have tried to get over this difficulty by suggesting that life forms capable of aerial locomotion may have evolved on Earth. In support of this rather far-fetched idea they argue that the dense atmosphere would make flying relatively easy; however, they gloss over the fact that the high gravity would have just the reverse effect. The conception of flying animals, though a charming one, is not taken seriously by any competent biologist.

More firmly based, however, is the theory that if any terrestrial animals exist, they will be found in the extensive oceans that cover so much of the planet. It is believed that life on our own world originally evolved in the ancient Martian seas, so there is nothing at all fantastic about this idea. On the oceans, moreover, the animals of Earth would no longer have to fight the fierce gravity of their planet. Strange though it is for us to imagine creatures that could live in water, it would seem that the seas of Earth may provide a less hostile environment than the land.

Quite recently, this interesting idea has received a setback through the work of the mathematical physicists. Earth, as is well known, has a single enormous moon, which must be one of the most conspicuous objects in its sky. It is some two hundred times the diameter of even the larger of our two satellites, and though it is at a much greater distance its attraction must produce powerful effects on the planet beneath it. In particular, what are known as 'tidal forces' must cause great movements in the waters of the terrestrial oceans, making them rise and fall through distances of many feet. As a result, all low-lying areas of the Earth must be subjected to twice-daily flooding; in such conditions, it is difficult to believe that any creatures could exist either in land or sea, since the two would be constantly interchanging.

To sum up, therefore, it appears that our neighbour Earth is a forbidding world of raw, violent energies, certainly quite unfitted for any type of life which now exists on Mars. That some form of vegetation may flourish beneath that rain-burdened, storm-tossed atmosphere is quite possible – indeed, many astronomers claim to have detected colour changes in certain areas which they attribute to the seasonal growth of plants.

As for animals – this is pure speculation, all the evidence being against them. If they exist at all, they must be extremely powerful and massively built to resist the high gravity, probably possessing many pairs of legs and capable only of slow movement. Their clumsy bodies must be covered with thick layers of protective armour to shield them from the many dangers they must face such as storms, fire, and the corrosive atmosphere. In view of these facts, the question of intelligent life on Earth must be regarded as settled. We must resign ourselves to the idea that we are the only rational beings in the Solar System.

For those romantics who still hope for a more optimistic answer, it may not be long before Planet Three reveals its last secrets to us. Current work on rocket propulsion has shown that it is quite possible to build a spacecraft that can escape from Mars and head across the cosmic gulf toward our mysterious neighbour. Though its powerful gravity would preclude a landing (except by radio-controlled robot vehicles), we could orbit Earth at a low altitude and thus observe every detail of its surface from little more than a millionth of our present distance.

Now that we have at last released the limitless energy of the atomic nucleus, we may soon use this tremendous new power to escape the bonds of our native world. Earth and its giant satellite will be merely the first celestial bodies our future explorers will survey. Beyond them lie . . .

[Unfortunately, the manuscript ends here. The remainder has been charred beyond decipherment, apparently by the thermonuclear blast that destroyed the Imperial Library, together with the rest of Oasis City. It is a curious coincidence that the missiles which ended Martian civilization were launched at a classic moment in human history. Forty million miles away, with slightly less advanced weapons, the Greeks were storming Troy. TRANSLATOR]

— 15 —

Son of Dr Strangelove
How I Learned to Stop Worrying and Love Stanley Kubrick

This essay was written for The Lost Worlds of 2001 *(1972) which contains not only a history of the film, but much material we didn't use in it. (Spielberg . . . Lucas . . . are you listening?)*

The first steps on the rather long road to *2001: A Space Odyssey* were taken in March 1964, when Stanley Kubrick wrote to me in Ceylon, saying that he wanted to do the proverbial 'really good' science-fiction movie. His main interests, he explained, lay in these broad areas: '(1) The reasons for believing in the existence of intelligent extraterrestrial life. (2) The impact (and perhaps even lack of impact in some quarters) such discovery would have on Earth in the near future.'

As this subject had been my main preoccupation (apart from time out for World War II and the Great Barrier Reef) for the previous thirty years, this letter naturally aroused my interest. The only movie of Kubrick's I had then seen was *Lolita*, which I had greatly enjoyed, but rumours of *Dr Strangelove* had been reaching me in increasing numbers. Here, obviously, was a director of unusual quality who wasn't afraid of tackling far-out subjects. It would certainly be worth while having a talk with him; however, I refused to let myself get too excited, knowing from earlier experience that the mortality rate of movie projects is about 99 per cent.

Meanwhile, I examined my published fiction for film-worthy ideas and very quickly settled on a short story called 'The Sentinel', written over the 1948 Christmas holiday for a BBC contest. (It didn't place.) This story developed a concept that has since been taken quite seriously by the scientists concerned with the problem of extraterrestrials, or ETs for short.

During the last decade, there has been a quiet revolution in scientific thinking about ETs; the view now is that planets are at least as common as stars – of which there are some hundred billion in our local Milky Way galaxy alone. Moreover, it is believed that life will arise automatically and inevitably where conditions are favourable; so there may be civilizations all around us which achieved space travel before the human race existed, and then passed on to heights which we cannot remotely comprehend . . .

But if so, why haven't they visited us? In my story 'The Sentinel' I proposed one answer (which I now more than half believe myself). We may indeed have had visitors in the past – perhaps millions of years ago, when the great reptiles ruled the Earth. As they surveyed the terrestrial scene, the strangers would guess that one day intelligence could arise on this planet; so they might leave behind them a robot monitor, to watch and to report. But they would not leave their sentinel on Earth itself, where in a few thousand years it would be destroyed or buried. They would place it on the almost unchanging Moon. And they would have a second reason for doing this. To quote from the original story:

They would be interested in our civilization only if we proved our fitness to survive – by crossing space and so escaping from the Earth, our cradle. That is the challenge that all intelligent races must meet, sooner or later. It is a double challenge, for it depends in turn upon the conquest of atomic energy, and the last choice between life and death.

Once we had passed that crisis, it was only a matter of time before we found the beacon and forced it open . . . Now we have broken the glass of the fire-alarm, and have nothing to do but to wait . . .

This, then, was the idea which I suggested in my reply to Stanley Kubrick as the take-off point for a movie. The finding – and triggering – of an intelligence detector, buried on the Moon aeons ago, would give all the excuse we needed for the exploration of the Universe.

By a fortunate coincidence, I was due in New York almost immediately, to complete work on the Time-Life Science Library's *Man and Space*, the main text of which I had written in Colombo. On my way through London I had the first chance of seeing *Dr Strangelove* and was happy to find that it lived up to the reviews. Its impressive technical virtuosity certainly augured well for still more ambitious projects.

It was strange, being back in New York after several years of living in the tropical paradise of Ceylon. Commuting – even if only for three stations on the IRT – was an exotic novelty, after my humdrum existence among elephants, coral reefs, monsoons and sunken treasure ships. The strange cries, cheerful smiling faces and unfailingly courteous manners of the Manhattanites as they went about their affairs were a continual source of fascination; so were the comfortable trains whispering quietly through the spotless subway stations, the advertisements (often charmingly adorned by amateur artists) for such outlandish products as Levy's bread, the *New York Post*, Piel's beer and a dozen fiercely competing brands of oral carcinogens. But you can get used to anything in time, and after a while (about fifteen minutes) the glamour faded.

My work in the Time-Life book division was not exactly onerous, since the manuscript was in good shape and whenever one of the researchers asked me, 'What is your authority for this statement?' I would look at her firmly and reply, 'I am.' So while *Man and Space* progressed fairly smoothly thirty-two floors above the Avenue of the Americas, I had ample energy for moonlighting with Stanley Kubrick.

Our first meeting took place at Trader Vic's, in the Plaza Hotel. The date – 22 April 1964 – happened to coincide with the opening of the ill-starred New York World's Fair, which might or might not be regarded as an unfavourable omen. Stanley arrived on time, and turned out to be a rather quiet, average-height New Yorker (to be specific, Bronxian) with none of the idiosyncrasies one associates with major Hollywood movie directors, largely as a result of Hollywood movies. (It must be admitted that he has since grown a full-fledged beard, which is one of his few concessions to modern orthodoxy.) He had a night-person pallor, and one of our minor problems was that he functions best in the small hours of the morning, whereas I believe that no sane person is awake after 10 p.m. and no law-abiding one after midnight. The late Peter George, whose novel *Red Alert* formed the basis of *Dr Strangelove*, once told me that Stanley used to phone him up for discussions at 4 a.m., desisting only when his bleary-eyed collaborator threatened to retreat to England. I am glad to say that he never tried this on me; in fact I would put consideration for other people as one of his most engaging characteristics – though this does not stop him from being absolutely inflexible once he has decided on some course of action. Tears, hysterics, flattery, sulks, threats of lawsuits will not deflect him one millimetre. I have tried them all: well, most of them . . .

Another characteristic that struck me at once was that of pure intelligence; Kubrick grasps new ideas, however complex, almost instantly. He also appears to be interested in practically everything; the fact that he never came near entering college, and had a less-than-distinguished high-school career, is a sad comment on the American educational system.

On our first day together, we talked for eight solid hours about science fiction, *Dr Strangelove*, flying saucers, politics, the space programme, Senator Goldwater – and, of course, the projected next movie.

For the next month, we met and talked on an average of five hours a day – at Stanley's apartment, in restaurants and cafés, cinemas and art galleries. Besides talking endlessly, we had a look at the competition. In my opinion there have been a number of good – or at least interesting – science-fiction movies in the past. They include, for example, the Pal–Heinlein *Destination Moon*, *The War of the Worlds*, *The Day the Earth Stood Still*, *The Thing* and *Forbidden Planet*. However, my affection for the genre perhaps caused me to make greater allowances than Stanley, who was highly critical of everything we screened. After I had pressed him to view H. G. Wells' 1936 classic *Things to Come*, he exclaimed in anguish, 'What *are* you trying to do to me? I'll never see anything you recommend again!'

Eventually, the shape of the film began to emerge from the fog of words. It would be based on 'The Sentinel' and five of my other short stories of space exploration; our private title for the project was 'How the Solar System Was Won'. What we had in mind was a kind of semi-documentary about the first pioneering days of the new frontier; though we soon left that concept far behind, it still seems quite a good idea. Later, I had the quaint experience of buying back – at a nominal fee – my unused stories from Stanley.

Stanley calculated that the whole project, from starting the script to the release of the movie, would take about two years, and I reluctantly postponed my return to Ceylon – at least until a treatment had been worked out. We shook hands on the deal during the evening of 17 May 1964, went out on to the penthouse veranda to relax – and at 9 p.m. saw, sailing high above Manhattan, the most spectacular of the dozen UFOs I've observed during the last twenty years.

It was also the only one I was not able to identify fairly quickly, which put me on the spot as I'd tried to convince Stanley that the wretched things had nothing to do with space. *This* one looked exactly like an unusually brilliant satellite; however, the *New York Times'* regular listing gave no transit at 9 p.m. – and, much more alarming, we felt convinced that this object came to rest at the zenith and remained poised vertically above the city for the best part of a minute before slowly sinking down into the north.

I can still remember, rather sheepishly, my feelings of awe and excitement – and also the thought that flashed through my mind: 'This is altogether too much of a coincidence. They are out to stop us from making this movie.'

What to do? When our nerves had ceased jangling, I argued that there must be a simple explanation, but couldn't think of one. We were reluctant to approach the Air Force, which was still smarting from *Strangelove* and could hardly be blamed if it regarded a report by two such dubious characters as a gag or a publicity stunt. But there was no alternative, so we apologetically contacted the Pentagon and had even gone to the trouble of filling in the standard sighting form – when the whole affair fizzled out.

My friends at the Hayden Planetarium set their computer to work and discovered that we had indeed observed an Echo 1 transit. Why this spectacular appearance wasn't listed in the *Times*, which gave two later and less impressive ones for the same night, was the only real mystery involved. The illusion that the object had hovered at the zenith almost certainly resulted from the absence of reference points in the brilliantly moonlit sky.

Of course, if it had been a *real* flying saucer, there would have been no movie. Some time later, Stanley tried to insure MGM against this eventuality with Lloyd's of London, asking them to draw up a policy which would compensate him if extraterrestrial life was discovered and our plot was demolished. How the underwiters managed to compute the premium I can't imagine, but the figure they quoted was appropriately astronomical and the project was dropped. Stanley decided to take his chances with the Universe.

This was typical of Stanley's ability to worry about possibilities no one else would think of. He always acts on the assumption that if something *can* go wrong, it will; ditto if it can't. There was a time, as the Mariner 4 space probe approached Mars, when he kept worrying about alternative story lines – just in case signs of life were discovered on the red planet. But I refused to cross that bridge until we came to it; whatever happened, I argued, we would be in fine shape. If there were Martians, we could work them in somehow – and the publicity for the movie would be simply wonderful.

Once the contracts had been signed, the actual writing took place in a manner which must be unusual, and may be unprecedented. Stanley hates movie scripts; like D. W. Griffith, I think he would prefer to work without one, if it were possible. But he had to have *something* to show MGM what they were buying; so he proposed that we sit down and first write the story as a complete novel. Though I had never collaborated with anyone before in this way, the idea suited me fine.

Stanley installed me, with electric typewriter, in his Central Park West office, but after one day I retreated to my natural environment in the Hotel Chelsea, where I could draw inspiration from the company of Arthur Miller, Allen Ginsberg, Andy Warhol and William Burroughs – not to mention the restless shades of Dylan and Brendan. Every other day Stanley and I would get together and compare notes; during this period we went down endless blind alleys and threw away tens of thousands of words.* The scope of the story steadily expanded, both in time and space.

During this period, the project had various changes of title: it was first announced as *Journey Beyond the Stars* – which I always disliked because there have been so many movie Voyages and Journeys that confusion would be inevitable. Indeed, *Fantastic Voyage* was coming up shortly, and Salvador Dali had been

---

*I saved lots of them in *The Lost Worlds of* 2001 (1972).

disporting himself in a Fifth Avenue window to promote it. When I mentioned this to Stanley, he said, 'Don't worry – we've already booked a window for you.' Perhaps luckily, I never took him up on this.

The merging of our streams of thought was so effective that, after this lapse of time, I am no longer sure who originated what ideas; we finally agreed that Stanley should have prime billing for the screenplay, while only my name would appear on the novel. Only the germ of the 'Sentinel' concept is now left; the story as it exists today is entirely new – in fact, Stanley was still making major changes at a very late stage in the actual shooting.

Our brainstorming sessions usually took place in the Kubrick East Side penthouse off Lexington Avenue, presided over by Stanley's charming artist wife Christiane, whom he met while making *Paths of Glory*. (She appears in its moving final scene – the only woman in the entire film.) Underfoot much of the time were the three – it often seemed more – Kubrick daughters, whom Stanley is in the process of spoiling. Very much a family man, he has little social life and begrudges all time not devoted to his home or his work.

He is also a gadget lover, being surrounded by tape recorders and cameras – all of which are well used. I doubt if even the most trigger-happy amateur photographer takes as many snapshots of his children as does Stanley – usually with a Pen D half-frame camera, which makes a slight contrast to the Cinerama-Panavision 70-millimetre monster he is manoeuvring most of the day. This would seem to suggest that he has no hobbies; it might be more true to say that they are integrated into his work.

He certainly has one absorbing recreation – chess, which he plays brilliantly; for a while he made a modest living at it, challenging the pros in Washington Square. Very fortunately, I long ago decided not even to learn the rules of this seductive game; I was afraid of what might happen if I did. This was very wise of me, for if we had both been chess players I doubt if *2001* would ever have been completed. I am not a good loser.

The first version of the novel was finished on 24 December 1964; I never imagined that two Christmases later we would *still* be polishing the manuscript, amid mounting screams of protest from publishers and agents.

But the first version, incomplete and undeveloped though it was, allowed Stanley to set up the deal. Through 1965, he gathered around him the armies of artists, technicians, actors, accountants and secretaries without whom no film can be made; in this case, there were endless additional complications, as we also needed scientific advisers, engineers, genuine space hardware and whole libraries of reference material. Everything was accumulated during the year at MGM's Borehamwood Studios, some fifteen miles north of London; the largest set of all, however, had to be built just six miles south of the city, at Shepperton.

Seventy years earlier, in the twelfth chapter of his brilliant novel *The War of the Worlds*, H. G. Wells' Martians had destroyed Shepperton with their heat ray. *This* year, man had obtained his first close-ups of Mars, via Mariner 4. As I watched our astronauts making their way over the lunar surface toward the ominously looming bulk of the Sentinel, while Stanley directed them through the radios in their space suits, I remembered that within five years, at the most, men would *really* be walking on the Moon.

Fiction and fact were indeed becoming hard to disentangle. I hope that in *2001: A Space Odyssey* Stanley and I added to the confusion, but in a constructive and responsible fashion. For what we were trying to create was a realistic myth – and we may well have to wait until the year 2001 itself to see how successful we have been.

— 16 —

The Myth of *2001*

The preceding article was written while 2001 *was still in production, when no one – not even Stanley – knew whether we were creating a masterpiece or a disaster, and the release date had been postponed so many times that some feared the title might have to be changed to* 2002.

The article which follows was done at the request of my old friend, and first professional editor, Walter Gillings, for the initial issue of his (alas) short-lived magazine Cosmos *(April 1969).*

After five years largely devoted to this single project, I still find myself much too close to it to look at it very objectively. Also, it is now obvious that there is far more in *2001* than I realized when we were making it; perhaps more indeed, than even Stanley Kubrick, its principal creator, had intended.

It is true that we set out with the deliberate intention of creating a myth. (The Odyssean parallel was clear in our minds from the very beginning, long before the title of the film was chosen.) A myth has many elements, including religious ones. Quite early in the game I went around saying, not very loudly, 'MGM doesn't know this yet, but they're paying for the first ten-million-dollar religious movie.' Nevertheless, it is still quite a surprise to see how many people realized this, and it has been amusing to see how many faiths have tried to stake claims in the finished work. Several reviewers have seen a cross in some of the astronomical scenes; this is purely a matter of camera composition. I might also mention that we have recently discovered – this was quite a shock – that there is a Buddhist sect which worships a large, black, rectangular slab! The analogy of the Kaaba has also been mentioned; though I certainly never had it in mind at the time, the fact that the Black Stone sacred to the Muslims is reputed to be a meteorite is a more than interesting coincidence.

All the mythical elements in the film – intentional and otherwise – help to explain the extraordinarily powerful responses that it has evoked from audiences and reviewers. In this we have been successful beyond our wildest dreams – certainly beyond mine! I have now read hundreds of reviews from newspapers and magazines all over the world (the most important of these, together with much other material, have appeared in New American Library's *The Making of Kubrick's* 2001, edited by Jerome B. Agel), and a pretty clear pattern of critical reaction is emerging.

A small number of reviewers said, even at first screening, that the movie was a masterpiece and a landmark in the history of the cinema. (Some have remarked flatly that it is 'obviously' one of the most important movies ever made.) Another small but significant proportion didn't like it the first time, wrote rather critical reviews, brooded for some days, went to see it again, and then wrote second reviews which were not only recantations but sometimes raves. This is the typical reaction to a new and revolutionary work of art (*vide* the first performance of *The Rite of Spring*), but in the past this process of evaluation took years or decades. I remember saying to Kubrick that he was luckier than Melville, who never lived to see the world appreciate *Moby Dick*.

Moby Dick, of course, has been mentioned many times in connection with 2001; though it is asking for trouble to make such comparisons, I had this work consciously in mind as a prototype (viz., the use of hard technology to construct a launch pad for metaphysical speculations). It took about half a century before literary criticism caught up with Melville; I wonder how many college theses are now being written on 2001.

Perhaps the majority of reviews were favourable but somewhat baffled, while another minority group was vociferously hostile. But this very hostility proves the emotional impact of the film; that acute critic Damon Knight (who has written that 2001 is 'undoubtedly one of the best films ever made') considers that the extraordinarily obtuse reaction of some science-fiction critics was simply due to embarrassment. They just couldn't face the film's religious implications.

There are others who, quite understandably, expected an updated *Destination Moon* and were baffled by Kubrick's version. But both time and the box office will prove that Kubrick was perfectly correct (indeed, the latter has already done so, for in almost all countries the film has been a fantastic commercial success). To have done a straightforward documentary-type movie – at the very moment when men were preparing to land on the Moon! – would have been to invite disaster, and would have provided no sort of artistic challenge. George Pal's *Destination Moon* was magnificent for 1950; we were interested in starting where that finished.

Soon after the movie was released, and the first cries of bafflement were being heard in the land, I made a remark that horrified the MGM top brass. 'If you understand *2001* on the first viewing,' I stated, 'we will have failed.' I still stand by this remark, which does not mean that one can't *enjoy* the movie completely the first time around. What I meant was, of course, that because we were dealing with the mystery of the Universe, and with powers and forces greater than man's comprehension, then by definition they could not be totally understandable. Yet there is at least one logical structure – and sometimes more than one – behind everything that happens on the screen in *2001*, and the ending does not consist of random enigmas, some simple-minded critics to the contrary. (You will find my interpretation in the novel; it is not necessarily Kubrick's. Nor is his necessarily the 'right' one – whatever that means.)

2001 has already become part of film history; it is the first science-fiction movie to do so, and its success has been so overwhelming that it poses the embarrassing problem 'Where do we go from here?' in a particularly acute form. Yet in a very few years it will probably seem old-fashioned, and people will wonder what all the fuss was about.

— 17 —

The Light of Common Day

This essay first appeared in Horizon *magazine (November 1963) and was reprinted in book form in* Voices *from the Sky (1966). I am particularly proud of the concluding paragraphs.*

No man has ever seen the Sun, or ever will. What we call 'sunlight' is only a narrow span of the entire solar spectrum – the immensely broad band of vibrations which the Sun, our nearest star, pours into space. All the colours visible to the eye, from warm red to deepest violet, lie within a single octave of this band – for the waves of violet light have twice the frequency, or 'pitch' if we think in musical terms, of red. On either side of this narrow zone are ranged octave after octave of radiations to which we are totally blind.

The musical analogy is a useful one. Think of one octave on the piano – less than the span of the average hand. Imagine that you were deaf to all notes outside this range; how much, then, could you appreciate of a full orchestral score when everything from contra-bassoon to piccolo is going full blast? Obviously you could get only the faintest idea of the composer's intentions. In the same way, by eye alone we can obtain only a grossly restricted conception of the true 'colour' of the world around us.

However, let us not exaggerate our visual handicap. Though visible light is merely a single octave of the Sun's radiation, this octave contains most of the power; the higher and lower frequencies are relatively feeble. It is, of course, no coincidence that our eyes are adapted to the most intense band of sunlight; if that band had been somewhere else in the spectrum, as is the case with other stars, evolution would have given us eyes appropriately tuned.

Nevertheless, the Sun's invisible rays are extremely important, and affect our lives in a manner undreamed of only a few years ago. Some of them, indeed, may control our destinies – and even, as we shall see in a moment, our very existence.

The visible spectrum is, quite arbitrarily, divided up into seven primary colours – the famous sequence, red, orange, yellow, green, blue, indigo, violet, if we start from the longest waves and work down to the shortest. Seven main colours in the one octave; but the complete band of solar radiations covers at least thirty octaves, or a total frequency range of ten thousand million to one. If we could see the whole of it, therefore, we might expect to discern more than two hundred colours as distinct from each other as orange is from yellow, or green is from blue.

Starting with the Sun's visible rays, let us explore outwards in each direction and see (though that word is hardly applicable) what we can discover. On the long-wave side we come first to the infra- red rays, which can be perceived by our skin but not by our eyes. Infra-red rays are heat radiation; go out of doors on a summer's day, and you can tell where the Sun is even though your eyes may be tightly closed.

Thanks to special photographic films, we have all had glimpses of the world of infra-red. It is an easily recognizable world, though tone values are strangely distorted. Sky and water are black, leaves and grass dazzling white as if covered with snow. It is a world of clear, far horizons, for infra-red rays slice through the normal haze of distance – hence their great value in aerial photography.

The further we go down into the infra-red, the stranger are the sights we encounter and the harder it becomes to relate them to the world of our normal senses. It is only very recently (partly under the spur of guided missile development) that we have invented sensing devices that can operate in the far infra-red. They see the world of heat; they can 'look' at a man wearing a brilliantly coloured shirt and smoking a cigarette – and see only the glowing tip. They can also look down on a landscape hidden in the darkness of night and see all the sources of heat from factories, cars, taxiing aircraft. Hours after a jet has taken off, they can still read its signature on the warm runway.

Some animals have developed an infra-red sense, to enable them to hunt at night. There is a snake which has two small pits near its nostrils, each holding a directional infra-red detector. These allow it to 'home' upon small, warm animals like mice, and to strike at them even in complete darkness. Only in the last decade have our guided missiles learned the same trick.

Below the infra-red, for several octaves, is a no man's land of radiation about which very little is known. It is hard to generate or to detect waves in this region, and until recently few scientists paid it much attention. But as we press on to more familiar territory, first we encounter the inch-long waves of radar, then the yard-long one of the shortwave bands, then the hundred-yard waves of the broadcast band.

The existence of all these radiations was quite unknown a century ago; today, of course, they are among the most important tools of our civilization. It is a bare twenty years since we discovered that the Sun also produces them, on a scale we cannot hope to match with our puny transmitters.

The Sun's radio output differs profoundly from its visible light, and the difference is not merely one of greater length. Visible sunlight is practically constant in intensity; if there are any fluctuations, they are too slight to be detected. Not only has the Sun shone with unvarying brightness throughout the whole span of human history, but we would probably notice no difference if we could see it through the eyes of one of the great reptiles.

But if you saw only the 'radio' Sun, you would never guess that it was the same object. Most of the time it is very dim – much dimmer, in fact, than many other celestial bodies. To the eye able to see only by radio waves, there would be little difference between day and night; the rising of the Sun would be a minor and inconspicuous event.

From time to time, however, the radio Sun explodes into nova brightness. It may, within *seconds*, flare up to a hundred, a thousand or even a million times its normal brilliance. These colossal outbursts of radio energy do not come from the Sun as a whole, but from small localized areas of the solar disc, often associated with sunspots.

This is one excellent reason why no animals have ever developed radio senses. Most of the time, such a sense would be useless, because the radio landscape would be completely dark – there would be no source of illumination.

In any event, 'radio eyes' would pose some major biological problems, because radio waves are millions of times larger than normal eyes, if they were to have the same definition. Even a radio eye which showed the world as fuzzily as a badly out-of-focus TV picture would have to be hundreds of yards in diameter; the gigantic antennas of our radar systems and radio telescopes dramatize the problem involved. If creatures with radio senses do exist anywhere in the Universe, they must be far larger than whales and can, therefore, only be inhabitants of gravity-free space.

Meanwhile, back on Earth, let us consider the other end of the spectrum – the rays shorter than visible light. As the blue deepens into indigo and then violet, the human eye soon fails to respond. But there is still 'light' present in solar radiation: the ultraviolet. As in the case of the infra-red, our skins can react to it, often painfully; for ultraviolet rays are the cause of sunburn.

And here is a very strange and little-known fact. Though I have just stated that our eyes do not respond to ultraviolet, the actual situation is a good deal more complicated. (In nature, it usually is.) The sensitive screen at the back of the eye – the retina, which is the precise equivalent of the film in a camera – does react strongly to ultraviolet. If it were the only factor involved, we could see by the invisible ultraviolet rays.

Then why don't we? For a purely technical reason. Though the eye is an evolutionary marvel, it is a very poor piece of optics. To enable it to work properly over the whole range of colours, a good camera has to have four, six or even more lenses, made of different types of glass and assembled with great care into a single unit. The eye has only one lens, and it already has trouble coping with the two-to-one range of wavelengths in the visible spectrum. You can prove this by looking at a bright red object on a bright blue background. They won't both be in perfect focus; when you look at one, the other will appear slightly fuzzy.

Objects would be even fuzzier if we could see by ultraviolet as well as by visible light, so the eye deals with this insoluble problem by eliminating it. There is a filter in the front of the eye which blocks the ultraviolet, preventing it from reaching the retina. The haze filter which photographers often employ when using colour film does exactly the same job, and for a somewhat similar reason.

The eye's filter is the lens itself – and here at last is the punch line of this rather long-winded narrative. If you are ever unlucky enough to lose your natural lenses (say through a cataract operation) and have them replaced by artificial lenses of clear glass, you will be able to see quite well in the ultraviolet. Indeed, with a source of ultraviolet illumination, like the so-called 'black light' lamps, you will be able to see perfectly in what is, to the normal person, complete darkness! I hereby donate this valuable information to the CIA, James Bond, or anyone else who is interested.

Normal sunlight, as you can discover during a day at the beach, contains plenty of ultraviolet. It all lies, however, in a narrow band – the single octave just above the visible spectrum in frequency. As we move beyond this to still higher frequencies, the scene suddenly dims and darkens. A being able to see only in the far ultraviolet would be in a very unfortunate position. To him, it would always be night, whether or not the Sun was above the horizon.

What has happened? Doesn't the Sun radiate in the far ultraviolet? Certainly it does, but this radiation is all blocked by the atmosphere, miles above our head. In the far ultraviolet, a few inches of ordinary air are as opaque as a sheet of metal.

Only with the development of rocket-borne instruments has it become possible to study this unknown region of the solar spectrum – a region, incidentally, which contains vital information about the Sun and the processes which power it by the atmosphere, miles above our head. In the far ultraviolet, if you started off from ground level on a bright, sunny day, this is what you would see.

At first, you would be in utter darkness, even though you were looking straight at the Sun. Then, about twenty miles up, you would notice a slow brightening, as you climbed through the opaque fog of the atmosphere. Beyond this, between twenty and thirty miles high, the ultraviolet Sun would break through in its awful glory.

I use that word 'awful' with deliberate intent. These rays can kill, and swiftly. They do not bother astronauts, because they can be easily filtered out by special glass. But if they reached the surface of the Earth – if they were not blocked by the upper atmosphere – most existing forms of life would be wiped out.

If you regard the existence of this invisible ultraviolet umbrella as in any way providential, you are confusing cause and effect. The screen was not put in the atmosphere to protect terrestrial life: it was put there by life itself, hundreds of millions of years before man appeared on Earth.

The Sun's raw ultraviolet rays, in all probability, did reach the surface of the primeval Earth; the earliest forms of life were adapted to it, perhaps even thrived upon it. In those days, there was no oxygen in the atmosphere; it is a by-product of plant life, and over geological aeons its amount slowly increased, until at last those oxygen-burning creatures called animals had a chance to thrive.

That filter in the sky is made of oxygen – or, rather, the grouping of three oxygen atoms known as ozone. Not until Earth's protective ozone layer was formed, and the short ultraviolet rays were blocked twenty miles up, did the present types of terrestrial life evolve. If there had been no ozone layer, they would doubtless have evolved into different forms. Perhaps we might still be here, but our skins would be very, very black.*

Life on Mars must face this problem, for that planet has no oxygen in its atmosphere and, therefore, no ozone layer. The far ultraviolet rays reach the Martian surface unhindered, and must profoundly affect all living matter there. It has been suggested that these rays are responsible for the colour changes which astronomers have observed on the planet. Whether or not this is true, we can predict that one of the occupational hazards of Martian explorers will be severe sunburn.

Just as ultraviolet lies beyond the violet, so still shorter rays lie beyond it. These are X-rays, which are roughly a thousand times shorter than visible light. Like the ultraviolet, these even more dangerous rays are blocked by the atmosphere; few of them come to within a hundred miles of Earth, and they have been detected by rocket instruments only during the last few years. The solar X-rays are quite feeble – only a millionth of the intensity of visible light – but their importance is much greater than this figure would indicate. We know now that blasts of X-rays from the Sun, impinging upon the upper atmosphere, can produce violent changes in radio communications, even to the extent of complete blackouts.

Men have lost their lives because the Sun has disrupted radio; nations are equally vulnerable, in this age of the ICBM.

You will recall that though the Sun shines with remarkable steadiness in the visible spectrum, it flares and sparkles furiously on the long (radio) waves. Exactly the same thing happens with its X-ray emission, even though these waves are a billion times shorter. Moreover, both the Sun's radio waves and its X-rays appear to

*I never imagined that, thirty years later, the ozone layer would be headline news!

come from the same localized areas of the solar surface – disturbed regions in the neighbourhood of sunspots, where clouds of incandescent gas larger than the Earth erupt into space at hundreds of miles a second.

For reasons not yet understood (there is not much about the Sun that we do thoroughly understand) solar activity rises and falls in an eleven-year cycle. The Sun was most active around 1957, which is why that date was chosen for the International Geophysical Year. In the 1960s it headed for a minimum but unfortunately threatened to come back to the boil at around the time the first major space expeditions were being planned. The astronauts might have run into some heavy weather, since the Sun by then was shooting out not only vast quantities of ultraviolet, X-rays and radio waves, but other radiations which cannot be so easily blocked. (As it turned out, however, the risks were far less than had at one time been feared.)

We see, then, how complicated and how variable sunlight is, if we use that word in the widest sense to describe all the waves emitted by the Sun. Nevertheless, when we accept the evidence of our unaided eyes and describe the Sun as a yellow star, we have summed up the most important single fact about it – at *this* moment in time. It appears probable, however, that sunlight will be the colour we know for only a negligibly small part of the Sun's history.

For stars, like individuals, age and change. As we look out into space, we see around us stars at all stages of evolution. There are faint blood-red dwarfs so cool that their surface temperature is a mere 4,000 degrees Fahrenheit; there are searing ghosts blazing at 100,000 degrees, and almost too hot to be seen, for the greater part of their radiation is in the invisible ultraviolet. Obviously, the 'daylight' produced by any star depends upon its temperature; today (and for ages past, as for ages to come) our Sun is at about 10,000 degrees Fahrenheit, and this means that most of its light is concentrated in the yellow band of the spectrum, falling slowly in intensity towards both the longer and the shorter waves.

That yellow 'bump' will shift as the Sun evolves, and the light of day will change accordingly. It is natural to assume that as the Sun grows older and uses up its hydrogen fuel – which it is now doing at the spanking rate of half a billion tons *a second* – it will become steadily colder and redder.

But the evolution of a star is a highly complex matter, involving chains of interlocking nuclear reactions. According to one theory, the Sun is still growing hotter and will continue to do so for several billion years. Probably life will be able to adapt itself to these changes, unless they occur catastrophically, as would be the case if the Sun exploded into a nova. In any event, whatever the vicissitudes of the next five or ten billion years, at long last the Sun will settle down to the white dwarf stage.

It will be a tiny thing, not much bigger than the Earth, and therefore too small to show a disc to the naked eye. At first, it will be hotter than it is today, but because of its minute size it will radiate very little heat to its surviving planets. The daylight of that distant age will be as cold as moonlight, but much bluer, and the temperature of Earth will have fallen to 300 degrees below zero. If you think of mercury lamps on a freezing winter night, you have a faint mental picture of high noon in the year AD 7,000 million.

Yet that does not mean that life – even life as we know it today – will be impossible in the Solar System; it will simply have to move in towards the shrunken Sun. The construction of artificial planets would be child's play to the intelligences we can expect at this date; indeed, it will be child's play to us in a few hundred years' time.

Around the year 10,000 million the dwarf Sun will have cooled back to its present temperature, and hence to the yellow colour that we know today. From a body that was sufficiently close to it – say only a million miles away – it would look exactly like our present Sun, and would give just as much heat. There would be no way of telling, by eye alone, that it was actually a hundred times smaller, and a hundred times closer.

So matters may continue for another five billion years; but at last the inevitable will happen. Very slowly, the Sun will begin to cool, dropping from yellow down to red. Perhaps by the year 15,000 million it will become a red dwarf, with a surface temperature of a mere 4,000 degrees. It will be nearing the end of the evolutionary track, but reports of its death will be greatly exaggerated. For now comes one of the most remarkable, and certainly least appreciated, results of modern astrophysical theories.

When the Sun shrinks to a dull red dwarf, it will not be dying. It will just be starting to live – and *everything that has gone before will be merely a fleeting prelude to its real history*.

For a red dwarf, because it is so small and so cool, loses energy at such an incredibly slow rate that it can stay in business for *thousands* of times longer than a normal-sized white or yellow star. We must no longer talk in billions but of trillions of years if we are to measure its life span. Such figures are, of course, inconceivable. (For that matter, who can think of a thousand years?) But we can nevertheless put them into their right perspective if we relate the life of a star to the life of a man.

On this scale, the Sun is but a week old. Its flaming youth will continue for another month; then it will settle down to a sedate adult existence which may last at least eighty years.

Life has existed on this planet for two or three days of the week that has passed; the whole of human history lies within the last second, and there are eighty years to come.

In the wonderful closing pages of *The Time Machine*, the young H. G. Wells described the world of the far future, with a blood-red Sun hanging over a freezing sea. It is a sombre picture that chills the blood, but our reaction to it is wholly irrelevant and misleading. For we are creatures of the dawn, with eyes and senses adapted to the hot light of today's primeval Sun. Though we should miss beyond measure the blues and greens and violets which are the fading afterglow of Creation, they are all doomed to pass with the brief billion-year infancy of the stars.

But the eyes that will look upon that all-but-eternal crimson twilight will respond to the colours that we cannot see, because evolution will have moved their sensitivity away from the yellow, somewhere out beyond the visible red. The world of rainbow-hued heat they see will be as rich and colourful as ours – and as beautiful; for a melody is not lost if it is merely transposed an octave down into the bass.

So now we know that Shelley, who was right in so many things, was wrong when he wrote:

> Life, like a dome of many-coloured glass,
> Stains the white radiance of eternity.

For the radiance of eternity is not white: it is infra-red.

— 18 —

How to Dig Space

Someone once defined a crank as an enthusiast without a sense of humour, and I have always believed that nothing is so important that you cannot make fun of it. (Perhaps I am the only person to joke about the end of the world: see 'No Morning After' in The Other Side of the Sky.*) At the same time, I must admit that I have occasionally been accused of having a schoolboy sense of humour, so you have been warned.*

This essay, believe it or not, originally appeared in the December 1964 Detroit Athletic Club News *– an important periodical in the days before the Japanese discovered the motor car.*

First of all, there are *two* kinds of space, and they mustn't be confused.

The old-fashioned variety, now badly dated, was discovered by a Greek named Euclid around 300 BC. Not only did he discover it; he found out more about it than any sensible person would want to know. Not until two thousand years later did one Nikolai Ivanovich Lobachevski (Russian, though you'd never guess it) find that Euclid had cheated by assuming half the things he'd pretended to prove. But by then the damage had been done.

Perhaps we'd better distinguish between the two types of space by spelling one of them with a capital. Small s space – the variety that Euclid got hung up on – is what stops everything from being in the same place. This definition has the simplicity of genius; I thought of it only five minutes ago.

So much for space; now about Space.

The biggest difference between Space and space is that there is so much more of the former. Yet, strangely enough, it is much more expensive. Unless you live in New York, space costs practically nothing. But even a smidgen of Space costs millions, which is why only rich and powerful nations like the United States and the Soviet Union can afford to buy it. This is very annoying for ex-r and p nations like Britain, who often go round telling everyone who'll listen that Space isn't worth it. Another Greek, Aesop, had a term for this: he called it sour grapes.

Until about three hundred years ago, nobody realized that there was so much Space, and the philosophers were very unhappy when Galileo showed it to them through his telescope. Some people tried to pretend it wasn't there, but this did not work. Ever since men started looking at Space, it has grown bigger and bigger. When last measured, it took twenty-two zeros to express its size, and you can bet that it's grown some more since then.

For a couple of hundred years, no one did much about Space except look at it. A few crazy writers – if that is not a tautology – wrote stories about going into Space. Nobody took them seriously, which was just as well because most of their Space stories were excuses to poke fun at the existing state of affairs. If the authors hadn't set their adventures in imaginary planets, they would have gone to very real prisons. (However, it is always dangerous to send authors to prison. This removes their chief excuse for not writing.)

At the beginning of the twentieth century there was a big change in the approach to Space. A Russian schoolteacher named Konstantin Tsiolkovsky started to write serious scientific papers about travelling into it. Presently he was followed by Robert Goddard, an American college professor, and Oberth, a Romanian high-school teacher. You will notice that all three pioneers of space travel were teachers: they were clearly trying to get away from *something*, and maybe it was the same in each case.

All these early studies of Space pointed to one answer – the rocket. The rocket had been known for about a thousand years, having been invented (like everything else) by the Chinese, though they didn't get round to it until AD 1200, which was rather late in the day for them. All this time, however, the rocket had been used only as a firework and a weapon. (Incidentally, there has been an unfortunate misunderstanding over the phrase 'The rocket's red glare'. It is widely believed in the United States that these were *British* rockets, but a careful search of British history books gives no evidence to support this ridiculous suggestion. It must have been another firm of the same name.)

The world's hard-headed, practical engineers were so busy copying their grandfathers' mistakes that it was about fifty years before they realized what Tsiolkovsky and Company were saying, and as usual it took a war to put across the message. However, when the German V2 started climbing to the edge of the atmosphere, it became rather difficult to ignore Space, though some people – as in Galileo's time – went right on trying.

But not in Russia, where Tsiolkovsky was a national hero. The USSR went full steam ahead to develop long-range rockets, using the results of the German war effort and as many of the engineers involved in it as could be rounded up. Unfortunately (or not, depending on the point of view), it couldn't get the top rocket experts. Almost without exception, they had been shipped to the United States, where they sat chewing their fingernails for five years while leading American scientists explained that intercontinental ballistic missiles were science fiction. The Russians happen to like science fiction, so they launched the first ICBM in 1957, and the first satellite a few months later. Though they get most upset when told that their Sputnik launchers were built by German scientists, this is entirely their own fault. They wouldn't release the names of their own top men, though everybody except the CIA knew that they were called Korolov,* Glushko, Tikhonravov, Kostikov, Dushkin and Robedonostev.

The discovery that the Russian satellites were about a hundred times as big as the American ones was, of course, a terrible blow to American pride, and vigorous steps were taken immediately to put matters right. These included setting up forty separate congressional committees on science and astronautics, so that all the top rocket scientists in the United States had to spend more than half

---

*Sergei Korolov's name emerged two years after this article was written, in 1966, when he was given a state funeral and revealed to be the hitherto anonymous 'chief designer' of the Soviet space programme. A (presumably) highly fictionalized movie of his life, *The Taming of Fire*, appeared in the early 1970s. Technically superb, especially in its historical reconstructions, perhaps the most astonishing thing about this film is the often unsympathetic, though in many ways admirable, character of the hero (he even fathers an illegitimate child). I don't know how the director got away with it, and perhaps he didn't.

their time giving evidence, preparing to give evidence, or recovering from giving evidence. Several million dollars were also appropriated for publicizing such reassuring statements as 'We are not engaged in a basketball game in space' and 'Well, it's just a hunk of iron' every time a new Sputnik went up.

It was seven years before the United States was able to launch a satellite bigger than the Russians' – and when they did so, most of the payload was five tons of Florida sand.* Later rockets will orbit used razor blades, thus solving one of the major problems of modern civilization.

This leads us at once to a question which is always of some interest to the taxpayer – the practical value of space research. Already it has produced thousands of valuable devices and discoveries which will soon make life easier for everyone. (These by-products used to be referred to as 'fall-out', but as that made everyone think of dandruff and H-bombs, the accepted term is now 'spin-off'. It is very popular with Air Force generals and top NASA brass, especially around budget time.) Here are just a few examples of spin-off:

Inertial guidance systems: These were developed to steer ICBMs to their targets and have now reached a fantastic degree of accuracy. With an inertial guidance system in your car, you need never be lost, even in Brooklyn. You merely set it to zero at your starting point and thereafter it tells you exactly where you are. This may not be the place you actually want to get to but, by heaven, you will know where it is, and all for less than a hundred thousand dollars. Of course, if you don't know where you've started from in the first place, that's too bad.

Computers: The so-called electronic brains are certainly the most spectacular, though not the noisiest, products of the Space Age. They can do the most elaborate calculations in a fraction of a second, and it is hard to imagine how we ever got along without them in the past. Every one of us, at some time or other, has known the acute embarrassment of being unable to remember the square root of π, to solve a ninth-order nonlinear partial differential

---

*Actually 11,500 pounds (Saturn 1 SA-5, 29 January 1964).

equation with complex coefficients, and similar household chores. Those days are now gone for ever.*

Miniaturization: Some electronic components are now so small that more time is spent looking for them than using them. The transistor radio, which has been such a blessing to all lovers of peace and quiet, will soon be no larger than a pinhead. This will make tuning a bit tricky, but you can't have everything.

Vacuum techniques: Since Space is practically empty, this means that enormous quantities of vacuum will soon become commercially available; in fact, the import of vacuum by space freighters will be one of the first astronautical industries. Vacuums, as everyone knows, have thousands of uses, from sucking up dust to keeping drinks warm (or cool) on picnics. They also provide the best possible soundproofing, and so will allow flats to be built with walls only a fraction of a centimetre thick, instead of almost a whole centimetre as at present. This will allow an extra quarter of a million people to live on Manhattan, and will increase the value of property everywhere. Portable vacuum sound-screens (probably collapsible) will be the only answer to the pin-sized transistor radios mentioned above.

Communications satellites: When these are perfected, the average man will have a choice of not less than ten thousand TV channels. Studies made by a leading Madison Avenue agency have already revealed some most interesting facts about the programmes they are likely to carry. For example, of the ten thousand channels, not less than six thousand will be devoted to Westerns, and about three thousand will deal with crime. Since these programmes will be broadcast over the whole world, travellers will no longer have to miss their favourite entertainment when they go abroad. Thus visitors to Switzerland or Bali won't have to spend hours looking at boring scenery; their portable TV sets will keep them in touch with the real world.

It has been calculated that, by the end of the century, every adult American will appear on a panel show at least once a month, and

---

*They certainly are. Who could have dreamed, back in 1964, that just ten years later millions of housewives would be able to tell you, in about two seconds, that root π is 1.772453851 and that slide rules and mathematical tables would be utterly obsolete?

because of the enormously increased importance of ratings and surveys, a whole new professional class will spring up – the full-time TV viewer. This will be a great boost to the economy, as it will absorb thousands of citizens who, owing to their low IQs, would be otherwise unemployable.

By the way, at least three of the ten thousand TV channels mentioned above will be largely devoted (apart from commercials) to educational and cultural matters.

Explosive-forming: This is a way of manufacturing quite complicated objects instantly by detonating suitably arranged charges of explosives. When this technique is perfected, you will be able to buy a prepackaged house which you can set down anywhere, light the fuse, and then walk in. When you're tired of it, you'll only have to buy some more explosives.

These are some of the down-to-earth applications of Space travel, but of course its most important result will be to take us to the other planets. And these are perfectly fascinating places.

Consider Mercury; when you go there, you'd better wear lightweight tropical clothing, as the thermometer can reach 750 degrees in the shade. And it's no good waiting for the cool evening breeze, because (a) there's no breeze and (b) there's no evening. The Sun always stays put in the same place, apparently stuck in the sky.* The only way to cool off is to go to the night side of the planet; and then you will cool off nicely, to about 400 degrees below zero. This is what the tourist leaflets call 'bracing'.

Venus, at the moment, is something of a mystery. (Actually, she's been a mystery for three hundred years, and the more we learn the more the mystery deepens.) Though she is further from the Sun than Mercury, she is almost as hot, owing to an atmosphere a hundred times as dense as Earth's. And she rotates backwards on her axis, which is something no other planet would dream of doing.

The fact that she is the only female in the Solar System may explain this contrary behaviour.

Then, of course, there is Mars. Unfortunately, Mars is full of Martians. Though there is considerable disagreement among

* A few years later it was discovered that Mercury does turn, slowly, beneath the Sun. The improvement in the weather is negligible.

writers on the subject, almost all are agreed that you wouldn't want a Martian to marry your sister. Even when they look remotely human, they usually have unflattering skin tones. (Green is a favourite colour.) Some have even more deplorable characteristics, like mouths in the palms of their hands, or gigantic tusks (see Edgar Rice Burroughs). Even worse were the Martians discovered by H. G. Wells, who looked rather like squashed octopods and were addicted to human blood. Against the prejudice generated by all this propaganda, the writings of the 'let's be friendly to the Martians' school, though headed by such able advocates as C. S. Lewis, Ray Bradbury and Robert Heinlein, have so far made very little headway.

Mars also presents a number of health hazards to visitors. Among the indigenous diseases are Cimmerian Swamp Rot, a fungus that grows with explosive violence and can turn a man into something resembling a hairy doormat in ten minutes flat. Mention should also be made of the Xanthean Brain Leech which burrows into the spinal cord and takes complete mental possession of its victim. Even more dangerous is a type of hypnotic squid found in the lowlands whose procedure makes the fabled sirens of Ulysses look like very small-time operators. By projecting irresistibly attractive visions into the mind of its prospective meal, it can lure any intelligent creature within range of its tentacles.

Life on Mars is tough, and one must be prepared for such little surprises.

The giant planets beyond Mars have fewer tourist attractions. Jupiter, the largest, is not the place to go if you are overweight; a terrestrial two hundred pounds would turn into about a quarter of a ton on Jupiter. The atmospheres are also slightly poisonous (hydrogen, methane, and – phew – ammonia) and are so dense that you could skin-dive in them. However, the views from the nearer moons are magnificent, especially in the case of Saturn.

It seems unlikely that the outer planets harbour any natives, friendly or otherwise. As in the case of Mars, however, writers on the subject have assumed the worst, and have created a whole legion of Bug-Eyed Monsters, familiarly known as BEMs. Whatever their shape (if, indeed, it remains fixed for more than a few minutes at a time), all BEMs have two characteristics in common.

They are implacably hostile; and they have an extraordinary and unquenchable interest in the female of the human species. Just what a BEM would do with one if it caught her has never been satisfactorily explained; in the interests of science, I cannot help wishing that some day a BEM would not be interrupted before it had finished whatever it wanted to do. A Society for the Prevention of Cruelty to BEMs seems well overdue.

I'd like to tell you a lot more about Space, but I'll have to break off here as something odd seems to be happening outside my window. There's a bright light flashing from a most peculiar object, hovering a couple of metres above the lawn, and I'd better investigate.

I can't imagine why such a ridiculous analogy popped into my mind – but it looks just like a saucer.

— 19 —

Last (?) Words on UFOs

I had refused to do reviewing for years because I knew perfectly well that most of the books sent to me would be by personal friends, and I did not wish to risk turning them into enemies. This does not deter professional reviewers, but they either are protected by a cloak of anonymity or have skins of rhinoceros hide.

But all rules must have occasional exceptions, and when the New York Times Book Review *asked if I would look at two of the very few serious books on UFOs, I rather nervously accepted the assignment. I had studied the subject for at least a decade before the unfortunate phrase 'flying saucer' came into circulation, and wanted to see if there was anything further to add to my essay 'Things in the Sky' (Report on Planet Three).*

Herewith the result, published in the New York Times Book Review, *27 July 1975 – including the footnote that I asked the* Times *to print. I am happy to say that the* Times *kept its side of the bargain, and I never received a single letter.*

And if this reprinting triggers any correspondence, it will not be read. After more than sixty years, starting with Charles Fort's Lo! *(1931), I am no longer interested in any further books, or letters, about UFOs.*

But I am still interested in UFOs themselves.
Mildly.

UFOs Explained. **By Philip J. Klass.** Illustrated. New York: Random House, 1974.

The UFO Controversy in America. **By David Michael Jacobs.** Foreword by J. Allen Hyneck. Illustrated. Bloomington & London: Indiana University Press, 1975.

One beautiful evening in the spring of 1964, Stanley Kubrick and I, after weeks of brainstorming, finally decided that we'd make a film about space. In a mood of cheerful exhilaration, we walked out on to Stanley's penthouse balcony to admire the view over Manhattan.

Suddenly, we noticed a brilliant star rising in the south. As it climbed steadily up the sky, I assumed it was the Echo balloon satellite – but to our astonishment, when it reached the zenith it apparently came to rest, hovering vertically above the city.*

We rushed indoors to collect Stanley's Questar. By the time we had set it up, the object was moving again, and we followed it for almost ten minutes before it disappeared over the northern horizon. But even through the telescope, it remained a featureless point of light.

Somewhat shaken, and clutching at the one remaining straw, we checked the daily listing of Echo transits in the *Times*. The satellite was not due for another hour . . .

Of the half-dozen UFOs I have seen (the first in the 1930s, long before anyone heard of 'flying saucers') this is the only one that ever made me lose any sleep, and reading these books brought it vividly back to mind. For no one who has not been through such an experience can really appreciate how a combination of unusual circumstances, inaccurate information and heightened emotional states can completely delude observers who consider themselves intelligent and level-headed.

Would you believe that the flaming fragments of a meteor or a re-entering satellite *a hundred miles away* would be mistaken by honest witnesses for a nearby vehicle with distinct rows of lighted windows (rectangular, at that!)? Philip Klass proves conclusively that this has happened not once, but several times. Will respectable, law-abiding citizens, often holding public office, fabricate photos and evidence? Same answer . . . No unbiased reader of *UFOs Explained* can doubt that, even when there is some real, external stimulus, much of the event reported lies in the mind of the beholder.

Yet the book's title is misleading. Though Mr Klass provides a welcome breath of sanity in a field where it is sadly lacking, he only explains some UFOs. From the multitudinous nature of the beasts,

*See Chapter 15, p. 150.

there will always be some that forever defy explanation, often because the truth is too ludicrous to be accepted. (Yes, Virginia, some UFOs are swamp gas. Some are owls. Some are bits of paper. Some are spiders' webs. And who would have believed a burning golf ball, releasing the explosive energy of its core as it bounded through the night?)

No wonder that the poor US Air Force was shot out of the sky when it went into battle with the UFOs, all Xerox machines firing. Dr Jacobs' scholarly study makes it abundantly clear that there was never any high-level 'conspiracy' to hide the 'facts' of extraterrestrial visitations, though one can hardly blame those who thought so at the time. The Air Force's pitiable attempts to sweep the whole annoying mess under the carpet, culminating in the hilarious shambles of the 'Condon Report', make pathetic reading.

So does the coldly factual demolition of the fakers and psychopaths who have bedevilled the subject; Dr Jacobs is content to let their own words condemn them. Lest we forget, thousands of nitwits believed George Adamski in 1955 when he 'flew' to the Moon and saw lakes, rivers and cities on the far side – now, of course, revealed in all its barren detail by American and Soviet cameras. But Adamski's successors are still in business; it's a pity there's no consumer-protection law giving, say, a thousandfold refund to purchasers of their demonstrably fraudulent books. Yet perhaps the various flying saucer cults provide a harmless hobby for unstable personalities. (I'm not referring, of course, to the many *serious* researchers who think that UFOs are important, and whose work is made so difficult by the crackpots.)

These two books are partly complementary, and belong in any library of the ten (to be generous) volumes worth reading on the subject of UFOs. Klass is a complete sceptic; Jacobs thinks that there may be a hard core of phenomena still unexplained by contemporary science. (This reviewer inclines to the same belief on Mondays, Wednesdays and Fridays.) One theory that can no longer be taken very seriously is that UFOs are interstellar spaceships. If there are as *few* as a million of these roaming round our Galaxy, I shall be very much surprised; but when they do turn up, we'll know in sixty seconds. They won't hang around for centuries, looking for a place to park.

Oh, I'm glad you asked. Our UFO turned out to be Echo, after all. For some extraordinary reason, the *Times* hadn't seen fit to print this splendid transit in its daily ephemeris, though two others were given that evening and simple arithmetic would have disclosed the third. The illusion that the object was hovering at the zenith had, like so many UFOs, multiple causes: (1) We were too excited to observe calmly; (2) it is almost impossible to judge the angular movement of anything vertically overhead; (3) bright moonlight had obliterated the star background which normally betrays satellite motion.

The whole incident once again underlines the only lesson we have so far learned from UFOs. They tell us absolutely nothing about intelligence elsewhere; but they do prove how rare it is on Earth.

Arthur Clarke, the science-fiction writer (*2001: A Space Odyssey*, and so on), is a resident of Sri Lanka. He believes that UFOs need a few decades of benign neglect, and threatens to sue *The Times* if it forwards any correspondence relating to this review.

Time for the Stars

This article was specially written for Voices from the Sky *(1966) and as far as I know has not appeared elsewhere.*

Every few years (Earth years) the subject of a Martian calendar crops up in the astronomical literature. There must be enough material now for a whole book on the subject.

Nothing in our lives is more basic, more unavoidable, than the ceaseless rhythm of night and day, or the regular progress of the seasons as the Earth makes its annual journey round the Sun. From the beginning of history, men have been conscious of time, and haunted by its meaning. It is not too fanciful to say that we have been born and bred inside a cosmic clock whose face is the pattern of stars, and whose hands are the Sun and the Moon. We have never been able to escape from it – until now.

It is about time (no pun intended) that we looked at some of the consequences of this escape from our particular cog in the celestial clockwork, the planet Earth. For we will soon have to learn that there is nothing fixed or sacred about days and weeks and years; not only do they differ from world to world, but there are even planets upon which such things will have no meaning.

Before we consider the strange clocks and calendars that the travellers and tourists of the future will need, let us have a brief glance at timekeeping here on Earth. We take date and time so much for granted that we often forget that it required thousands of years, and some of the finest minds the human race has ever produced, to establish our present system of timekeeping or chronology.

The basic unit of time is, of course, the day. The concept of the day is not merely obvious, it is unavoidable. Even the simplest animals are aware of the difference between light and darkness, though it took mankind a great many centuries to discover that the effect was due to the spin of the Earth on its axis, not to an actual movement of the Sun across the sky.

Quite arbitrarily, we divide the day into twenty-four hours. Let us be absolutely clear on this point. Hours (and their subdivisions, minutes and seconds) are the inventions of man, and have no counterparts in the natural world. We might say that God made the day, and the rest is the work of man. The day might just as well have been split into ten or a hundred parts, though twenty-four has certain purely numerical advantages, since it can be conveniently divided into thirds, quarters, sixths, eights and twelfths.

Equally arbitrary are the week and the month; were it not for the accident that we have a single bright Moon that takes a little more than seven days to change from quarter to quarter, and nearly thirty to go through the full cycle of its phases, we might not have settled upon either interval. As the Earth is the only planet with a single moon* (all the others have none or several) it is quite clear that the month is a quaint local custom; but it is a convenient one which we will probably export elsewhere.

The year, on the other hand, is quite another matter. It is as fundamental, as inescapable, as the day, and dominates human, animal and plant life to an equally marked extent especially in high latitudes, where summer and winter bring such changes that they might almost be in different worlds. Even near the Equator, where there is little change of temperature with the seasons, the cycle of the year still makes itself felt, for it brings such regular variations of wind and rain as the famous 'monsoons'. Nowhere on Earth can we escape from the effects of our planet's annual march around the Sun.

The day and the year are, therefore, the two natural and basic intervals of time; we have to accept them as they are and somehow incorporate them into our systems of chronology.

All would be well – or fairly well – if the day went into the year an exact number of times. Unfortunately it doesn't, and this stubborn fact has given calendar makers headaches for at least five thousand years.

---

*Pluto is now known to have one, Charon.

Probably the first rough estimate, soon after men learned to count at all, was that the year lasted 360 days, which gives a beautifully simple calendar of twelve 30-day months. Unfortunately, such a calendar goes haywire very rapidly, because the Earth actually takes a little more than 365 days to complete one circuit around the Sun. If you start counting off 360-day 'years', therefore, you get out of step with the seasons at the rate of five days every year. After only thirty-six years you're six months out of phase and are celebrating Christmas at midsummer – unless you've starved to death first because your crop planting has been equally in error. For an accurate calendar is not merely a social convenience; it is a matter of life and death. Agricultural man knew this very well, as he watched the star patterns that marked the coming of spring; but supermarket man tends to forget it.

A 365-day calendar is a great improvement, and a 365¼-day one is better still. This, of course, is the one we use, by the simple dodge of inserting an extra day every fourth (leap) year. If the Earth took precisely 365 days and 6 hours to go around the Sun, this calendar would be correct for ever. As the year is actually a little shorter than 365¼ days, additional adjustments are necessary from time to time, but only at very long intervals. (Still, it's amazing how these errors can add up, like dust swept under the carpet, if you don't do something about them. By 1752 the calendar was no less than eleven days out of kilter, and it was therefore necessary to decree that 2 September would be followed by 14 September. I suspect that most politicians would be very embarrassed, even now, if they had to face the cry that then went up from the indignant populace: 'Give us back our eleven days!')

So much, then, for the basic principles of time measurement on the planet Earth; now we are ready to face the peculiar things that happen off it. Peculiar to us, that is; to other beings, if they exist, we will be the oddities, with our comic clocks and calendars.

The first astronauts have already encountered some of the problems of timekeeping in space, for they have experienced a 90-minute day. This is the time that a close satellite, like a Mercury capsule, takes to go around the Earth. Every hour and a half, therefore, a traveller in such a capsule witnesses a sunrise; every hour and a half he sees a sunset. He learns, as no men have ever done before, that daytime and night-time are private experiences; they depend on where you are and how fast you are moving. Night itself is purely a local effect – the temporary eclipse of the Sun by the shadow of a planet. The further our orbiting astronauts travel into space, the less they will see of night. When they are thousands of miles out, they will hardly ever pass through Earth's narrow cone of shadow; they will be in eternal light – perpetual day. They will always see the Sun shining in their sky.

Space travellers en route will be in much the same situation as submariners during a prolonged undersea voyage. They can use whatever method of timekeeping suits their convenience; whether it is day or night outside the walls of their vessel scarcely concerns them. Almost certainly, astronauts will adopt Greenwich Mean Time (GMT), as thousands of navigators at all heights and depths all over the world are doing at this very moment. Spaceships will carry incredibly accurate clocks, measuring the passage of time by the unvarying vibrations of atoms, not the oscillations of balance-wheels, which are subject to all sorts of irregularities. Such atomic clocks can measure time to an accuracy of a few parts in a million million; it would take tens of thousands of years for them to gain or lose a single second!

The simple solution of using GMT, unfortunately, breaks down as soon as we land on any other planet. For then we will no longer be living in our own private little world, and it becomes essential to have clocks and calendars which bear some relation to the natural events taking place around us. The scientists may stick to GMT, but future planetary colonists would like to have clocks that will at least tell them whether the Sun is shining out of doors. And this is where the trouble begins.

It will start first on the Moon, though the situation there is not as bad as it might be. Since Earth and Moon form a single closely knit little family, they go around the Sun together and so have the same year. The lunar 'day', however, is extremely long – just over twenty-nine and a half of our days.

It is hardly likely that human beings will ever adapt themselves to fifteen days of wakefulness and fifteen days of sleep, nor will it be necessary. But it will be necessary to have clocks which show the slow progress of the Sun across the lunar sky, and you may be surprised to know that such time-pieces can be bought at any good watchmakers. You may even be wearing one at this very moment.

Those watches that show the phases of the Moon will be very handy on the Moon. They could be easily set so that the changing crescent gave an approximate answer to the vital question, 'How many days till sunset?' And on this side of the Moon there would, of course, be another timekeeper always visible in the sky. As it went through its phases – the exact reverse of those that the Moon shows to us – the huge and brilliant Earth would tell the experienced traveller just what time of lunar day it was. For when the Earth is full, the Moon is new, and vice versa.

It is when we get to Mars that things start to become really complicated. In the first place, the Martian day is not the same length as ours, though it is surprisingly close to it – about twenty-four hours and forty minutes. This is not too bad as far as working schedules are concerned, and it would be simple to modify an ordinary watch so that it ran slow enough to keep good Martian time. (Before you try it, I should mention that the usual regulators seldom allow you to lose the necessary forty minutes a day. Few watchmakers expect their products to be that much in error.) The explorers would soon adapt themselves to the slightly stretched twenty-four-hour clock, and even that sensitive timekeeper, the human stomach, would not be inconvenienced by the extra five or ten minutes between meals.

We cannot, however, dispose of the Martian calendar so easily. It takes almost two Earth years (to be more precise, 686.979702. . . days) for Mars to make one revolution around the Sun. But we're not concerned with the number of Earth days in the Martian calendar – only the number of *Mars* days, which is obviously a little smaller. It's actually 668.599051. What, you may well ask at this point, will a 668.599051-day calendar look like?

Well, at least two astronomers – Dr R. S. Richardson of Mount Palomar and Dr I. M. Levitt of the Fels Planetarium, Philadelphia – have attempted to construct one. Assuming that we stick to twelve months so that we can retain the familiar names January, February and so on, each quarter of the Martian year might contain one 55-day and two 56-day months. This is much neater than the messy calendar we have inherited from Julius Caesar and

Pope Gregory XIII, though it would be rather a long time between pay cheques.

Four quarters of 167 days each give a 668-day year, which is almost exactly 0.6 days short of the actual Martian year. To correct this, we need rather a lot of leap years – obviously, six in every ten, or three in every five, as compared to one in four on Earth. However, this calendar would be accurate over extremely long intervals; no further corrections would be needed for a thousand years.

Reconciling terrestrial and Martian calendars will be a complicated and tedious job, and no doubt the interplanetary diaries of the future will contain tables so that you can compare dates at a glance. Dr Levitt has done better than this; in co-operation with the Hamilton Watch Company, he has designed a clock to show both the time and the date on Earth and Mars. When this clock was built several years ago, I am sure that neither the doctor nor the company realized how soon it would be needed.

Incidentally, from what point in time will we start reckoning the Martian calendar? It will make the task of future historians easier if we begin Year 1 with the first landing. This would also reduce the risks of confusion between the two calendars. A date like 14 March 5 will hardly belong to Earth – and there would be no doubt at all in a case like February 47.

But even with the greatest care on both worlds, there are bound to be difficulties and mistakes as Earth–Mars traffic and trade increase. Here are some of the problems that lurk in ambush for the next generation, and perhaps for some who read these words, since the first landing on Mars cannot be much more than twenty years away.*

By the Mars calendar, 50 will be a ripe old age, since it will correspond to 94 years on Earth. Martian colonists will be able to vote at 11, marry at 9. A change of residence from Earth to Mars, or vice versa, would produce frightful complications. Although the biological rate of ageing will, we assume, be the same on both worlds, a colonist returning to Earth would start clocking up birthdays almost twice as quickly as if he had stayed on Mars.

---

*Alas, it is *still* twenty years away.

Tourists of the future will simply have to get used to the fact that calendars, as well as currencies, can have different rates of exchange. The lawyers are going to have a field day drafting time clauses in interplanetary contracts.

Even when they stay at home and don't try to do business with Earth, the Martians (let's drop that snooty 'colonial' tag, shall we?) will have troubles of their own. The long months and the numerous leap years have already been mentioned, but one could grow accustomed to these. A subtler problem is one which was first encountered by terrestrial explorers more than four hundred years ago, and is probably destined to cause many headaches on Mars.

On 7 September 1522, the exhausted survivors of Magellan's expedition landed in Spain after circumnavigating the globe for the first time in the history of mankind. As soon as they did so, they made a horrible discovery, doubly distressing to good Catholics who paid due regard to Saints' Days. By their careful reckoning, it was only the 6th, not the 7th, of September; somewhere, they had lost a day . . .

I am by no means sure that, even now (and even after seeing *Around the World in Eighty Days*, where Phileas Fogg *gained* a day by travelling in the opposite direction from Magellan), many people could give a clear explanation of what happens when one crosses the International Date Line. (Don't worry; I'm not going to give one, either.) We all know that the thing exists, and that it has been safely parked in the middle of the Pacific Ocean so that it causes the minimum of inconvenience to everyone – except to travellers jetting between Asia and America, who frequently find they've arrived before they started.

The Martians – some of them, anyway – will be in an even worse plight. As there are no oceans on the planet, their International Date Line will have to lie on land. This means that, somewhere on Mars, some time in the future, there will be a street or a square or a city park where it's Friday on one side and Saturday on the other. It will be quite a tourist attraction, but a great nuisance to the people who have to live with it. Can you imagine what it would be like in your town, if the date changed when you crossed the road? The fact that this doesn't happen in some residential area on Earth is pure luck; it must occur on all inhabited planets that do not possess convenient oceans in which unwanted days can be drowned. I have used this idea in a short story, 'Trouble with Time', which you will find in *Tales of Ten Worlds*.

Yet if you think that the Martians have problems, wait until you get to Jupiter.

So far, the worlds we've considered all have one thing in common. Their 'days' may be of different lengths, but at least they are the same everywhere on the planet. This is no longer true on Jupiter, for this giant among the Sun's children does not revolve as a solid body – it turns more rapidly at the Equator than at higher latitudes. If you lived in the Jovian tropics (not that they are very tropical, almost half a billion miles from the Sun) you would find that the day lasted about nine hours and fifty minutes of our time. But as you went north or south towards the poles, it would lengthen by approximately five minutes.

This means, of course, that Jupiter has no fixed geography; its surface is plastic so that regions in higher latitudes slowly drift backwards as the planet spins. To imagine such a state of affairs on the Earth, you must picture a situation in which Canada and South America steadily move westward with respect to the United States. This may indeed actually happen, but it takes geological ages – not millions, but hundreds of millions, of years – for the effect to be noticeable. On Jupiter, it requires only a few months, so both timekeeping and map-making on the planet involve fearful complications.

Fortunately, these problems may never be of much practical importance, for Jupiter is one planet that human explorers will probably be glad to leave alone. An atmosphere of hydrogen, methane and ammonia, at pressures rising to millions of tons to the square inch and ripped by thousand-mile-an-hour winds, is not an attractive prospect, especially when coupled with a gravity two and a half times Earth's and temperatures approaching three hundred below zero. Any tourist agency preparing a travel folder on Jupiter will have to overwork that useful adjective 'bracing'.

However, even if we leave the exploration of Jupiter to robot space probes, we will certainly land on the planet's dozen or more moons, several of them large enough to count as worlds in their own right. (Ganymede and Callisto, for example, are almost as big as

Mars.) As they all accompany Jupiter on his journey around the Sun, they will share his year, which is eleven years and ten months of our time. A single 'month' of Jovian time would thus last as long as an Earth year.

As we move still further outwards beyond Jupiter, the planetary years become ever longer, approximately doubling as we jump from one world to the next. Saturn takes 29½ years to complete its circuit around the Sun; Uranus, 84; Neptune, 165; and Pluto, the most distant of the planets, no less than 248.

On such remote worlds, the conception of the year can have little meaning. There will be no seasons, for the temperature is always hundreds of degrees below zero. The Sun is little more than an exceptionally brilliant star, providing plenty of light, but no heat. On Pluto, the noonday sun would be about as warm as our full moon.

The 'days' of the outer planets present us with a curious paradox. The larger the world, the shorter its day – not, as you might reasonably expect, the other way around. We have already mentioned Jupiter's flexible 9 hours 50 to 9 hours 55-minute day; Saturn revolves in 10 hours 14 minutes, Uranus in 10 hours 49 minutes, Neptune in (probably) 14 hours. Little Pluto, on the other hand, has a slow day, six and a half times longer than ours.

I suspect that for the giant planets and their many satellites, we will stick to Earthly calendars and clocks, just as we will do aboard our spaceships. Any settlements we may establish on the outskirts of the Solar System must, of course, be completely sealed from their ferociously hostile surroundings. The rapid daily sweep of the Sun across the sky, and its slow annual crawl around the zodiac, will have none of the significance that they do on Earth.

It will be far otherwise when we travel in towards the heart of the Solar System. On the two inner planets, Venus and Mercury, the Sun is the dominant factor in life, and its movements must be all-important. As on Earth, Moon and Mars we will once again have to adjust our clocks and calendars to local conditions.

Our next-door neighbour Venus has a short year of 225 days. The Venusian (Cytherean? Venerian? Take your choice) day is, however, a major mystery.* Because the planet is perpetually veiled in

---

*No longer. Radar has revealed the surprising facts that Venus has a 'day' of 243 Earth days, and Mercury one of 58.6.

clouds, no definite surface features have ever been observed from which the rate of rotation can be deduced. Indirect evidence suggests that Venus takes at least ten Earth days, and perhaps considerably longer, to rotate on her axis. If this is the case, there will be fewer than twenty Venus days in the Venus year. There may be only one. However, the observations of Mariner 1 indicate that the atmosphere of Venus is so dense and opaque that no sunlight ever reaches the almost red-hot surface of the planet. In that case, we have a situation like that in the depths of our own oceans. More than a mile down in the sea, by day or night, there is perpetual darkness. The abyss knows nothing of the Sun; so it may be with Venus.

On Mercury, the planet nearest to the Sun, we will encounter a situation that is almost baffling in its simplicity. This welcome change arises from the fact that the planet keeps one side always turned towards the Sun, so that the very conceptions of night and day, sunrise and sunset, have no meaning there. On one hemisphere there is eternal light, on the other, eternal darkness. The only measure of time that has any significance on Mercury is the year, which lasts a mere 88 Earth days.

It is hard for us to imagine a world which will know nightfall only when the Sun itself expires. If you wish to see night on Mercury, it is no good waiting for it – you must travel to the dark side of the planet, until the Sun sinks below the horizon.

And there you will meet a night indeed, unmatched elsewhere in the Solar System. The Mercurian night has lasted, in all probability, since life first emerged upon the face of our planet. It must be cold beyond imagination, not far above the absolute zero of temperature. Yet it will be a night glorious with stars and dominated by two beautiful apparitions – the electric blaze of Venus and the scarcely less brilliant double-star formed by the twin worlds Earth and Moon.*

We have now completed the roll-call of the Solar System, apart from such unimportant bodies as comets and asteroids. But we have scarcely begun to examine all the possibilities that exist in this

---

*The discovery that Mercury rotates with respect to the Sun has, unfortunately, wiped out a whole category of science-fiction stories.

incredible Universe of ours, so I would like to look at one more astronomical situation – perhaps the hardest of all for our minds to grasp.

Whatever their individual differences, the planets of *this* Solar System do have one thing in common: they all go around the Sun, and so each experiences a year of a fixed and definite length ranging, as we have seen, from 88 days in the case of Mercury to 248 years in the case of Pluto.

The key phrase in that last sentence is *they all go around the Sun*. But the planets of other solar systems may not go around a sun; they may have half a dozen from which to choose . . .

For our Sun is a cosmic recluse, wending its lonely way millions of millions of miles from its nearest stellar neighbour. Most stars, on the other hand, are sociable, occurring in pairs, triplets, or even more complicated family groups. Any planets of such stars cannot move in simple, approximately circular orbits that repeat themselves regularly, age after age. The conflicting tugs and pulls of the ever-changing gravitational fields in which they move make this quite impossible.

The planets of multiple star systems must travel on strange, looping curves of inconceivable complexity that will never repeat themselves again as long as the Universe endures. Look at the curves around the border of a banknote: the mathematics of those is utterly childish in comparison.

When there are many suns in the sky, crawling along different paths and rising and setting at different times, it is no longer possible to speak of either days and years; the terms are as empty of meaning as colour to a blind man. The inhabitants of such worlds, should any exist, must invent mechanical devices if they wish to measure time. There will be no celestial clocks in the heavens, no regular and predictable movement of a single sun and a single moon across the background of the stars. The very concept of time might never be discovered on such worlds. And perhaps, because of that, their inhabitants will know nothing of our obsession with change and decay; they will neither dream of the future nor yearn for the past. Living in an eternal present, they will have conquered time – by ignoring it.

— 21 —

The Meddlers

This originally appeared in Playboy *magazine (March 1964) and in book form in 1966. Its prediction of a certain press release 'around about the year 1990' has proved a bit premature; but let's push it back to 2000, and see what happens then. If we're still around . . . (JB)*

From his simian ancestors, man has inherited an insatiable itch to meddle with his surroundings. There is a straight and unbroken line of evolution between a cageful of monkeys in the zoo and the Atomic Energy Commission in the Pacific.

Now a certain amount of meddling is an excellent thing; it laid the foundations of experimental science and of modern technology. But the intelligent meddler must abide by a few common-sense rules, of which the most important are:

    1. Do not attempt the unforeseeable.
    2. Do not commit the irrevocable.

Though these rules have often been broken, in the past it seldom mattered; for the damage was confined to the meddler and his immediate vicinity. This is no longer the case; the consequences of meddling are now global, and will soon be astronomical.

I have no wish for my typewriter to add to the literary fall-out on Fall-out, but my first example has to be the Bravo explosion of 1 March 1954, which showered radioactive coral upon the trawler *Lucky Dragon* – miles outside the 'safety zone' confidently established by the meteorologists. In many ways, this event set the pattern for the future; those responsible were embarrassed, and hurried to compensate the injured, but showed no particular signs of remorse. Too bad about those fishermen, but little sacrifices like that have to be made for the safety of the United States.

Then followed the long dialogue of hypocritical self-interest between the USSR and the US on the subject of bomb testing, each claiming the right to contaminate the Earth in pursuance of its policy of massive suicide. As a result, every living human being is now appreciably more radioactive than his or her grandparents – with incalculable effects upon all the generations to come. Contrary to the science-fiction writers, fall-out will not produce a crop of monstrous mutants; extreme variations from the norm have little chance of survival, and less of reproduction. But it will produce an endless series of minor defects, illnesses and premature deaths which, all told, will add up to a staggering sum of human misery.

Two centuries ago Nathan Hale might regret that he had but one life to give for his country; today's patriots must ask themselves how many genes (and whose) they are prepared to give for theirs. And although the US–USSR pact on bomb testing is a welcome step toward sanity, who can say how much damage has already been done?

Quite apart from fission products, our modern world is drenched with chemicals which did not exist ten or twenty years ago. Almost all of them – DDT and the other insecticides, penicillin and its related 'wonder drugs' – involve some degree of risk. In most cases, we accept these risks willingly: penicillin has saved thousands of lives for every one jeopardized by allergic reactions; pets and people may have been poisoned by DDT, but it has eliminated typhus and malaria from whole countries. No one but a madman would deny these benefits, yet we must never become complacent and overconfident. Rachel Carson's strident warning, in *Silent Spring*, was necessary, even if exaggerated, though E. B. White saw the danger years before in his unforgettable *The Morning of the Day They Did It*. That satirical fantasy, now rapidly coming true, described a world where the chemists had made agricultural products so plentiful – and so toxic – that everyone had to take regular injections to counteract the lethal effects of food.

The terrible Thalidomide disaster has alerted everyone to these dangers, for the moment. It has been pointed out that if Thalidomide had been developed in the United States, instead of Europe, 'the marketing techniques of the pharmaceutical industry, which can saturate the country with a new drug almost as soon as it leaves the laboratory, would have enabled Thalidomide to produce thousands of deformed infants' (Helen B. Taussig, *Scientific American*, August 1962). The United States escaped this catastrophe by good luck and the timely warning of Dr Kelsey; next time, it may not be so fortunate.

For there will be a next time – though no one knows where and when. The price of safety, as of liberty, is eternal vigilance. The people to watch are the pharmaceutical firms out for a quick buck, and the defence scientists out for a big bang.

Not that nuclear explosions are the only global nuisances committed, or attempted, in the name of security. Perhaps you never heard about Project West Ford, the bright idea of MIT's Lincoln Laboratories to put a third of a billion tiny radio antennas into orbit. When they learned about it, the world's astronomers reacted with near-unanimous violence, protesting that this cloud of minute satellites would interfere with many types of fundamental research for an indefinite period to come. Despite an appeal by the International Astronomical Union to the US Government, the experiment went ahead in October 1961.

The first attempt failed, but success was achieved in May 1963. There are rumours of other launchings; a recent issue of the authoritative space journal *Astronautics* comments on an unexplained US Air Force satellite with these ominous words: 'It is difficult to avoid the conclusion that the Air Force is quietly placing additional dipoles in orbit.'*

The most controversial, and widely criticized, of all space experiments took place in mid-Pacific on 8 July 1963, when despite a series of launching mishaps that would have discouraged less devoted experimenters, the AEC and the Department of Defense detonated a megaton bomb two hundred miles above Johnston Island. (Sociological note: in the press releases, it's always a 'nuclear device'. I say it's a bomb, and I say the hell with it.) Once again, there had been a chorus of protests from scientists all over the

---

*It is only fair to report that this story has a happy ending. Before the second West Ford (originally known as 'Needles') experiment was carried out, it was fully analysed by international committees of leading scientists. They predicted the conditions under which it would be harmless, and the authorities responsible conducted it accordingly. Let us hope that this sets a precedent for future experiments of a global (or cosmic) nature.

world; once again, the objectors were made to appear alarmists by bland official statements. There was not the slightest risk, everyone was assured, that the Van Allen belts, which had been around for several billion years, would be blown up within five years of their discovery.

Well, the belts are still there, though somewhat groggy. The confident calculations were out by a factor of ten, possibly a hundred. (The argument is still in progress.) Three artificial satellites, placed in orbit at enormous expense, were promptly silenced – or at least muffled – by the unexpectedly powerful blast of radiation. One of them happened to be the very first British-built satellite, kindly launched only a few weeks earlier by the US Space Administration as part of its well-intended programme of international co-operation.

I can only mention in passing (and passing is what we probably are) such 'Coming Attractions' as the neutron bomb, laser heat rays, and the *really* virulent diseases that the biological warriors will be able to design, when the genetic code has been cracked and we can create organisms that nature never imagined. One would expect such activities to cause trouble; but unfortunately, even 'harmless' experiments, on the scale at which we are now operating, may lead to most peculiar and obscure disasters. For example: The only thing that protects you from a painful death by acute sunburn is a thin layer of ozone, twenty miles above your head. The amount involved is very small, but it almost completely absorbs the Sun's lethal ultraviolet rays. Now, in the course of our space experiments, we are dumping enormous quantities of exotic chemicals into the upper atmosphere – quantities which, in some cases, will exceed the amounts of gas already there. This is contamination with a vengeance, and no one knows what its results will be. A generation from now, that ultraviolet may start leaking through the ozonosphere roof, and we'll have to move underground.*

Where is this going to lead, as our powers over nature, but not over ourselves, continue to increase? If we extrapolate the present trends in technological megalomania, arrogant ignorance and national selfishness, this is the type of press release we may expect from the Pentagon, around about the year 1990:

*This paragraph, written in 1964, may be one of the first 'ozone hole' warnings.

As there has been much ill-informed criticism of the US Space Force's proposed attempt to extinguish the Sun by means of the so-called 'Blackout Bomb' (Operation Pluto), the following statement is being issued to reassure the public.

The experiment is based on the discovery by Spitzer, Richardson, Chandrasekhar and others that the injection of polarized neutrinos into a certain class of sunspot can start a chain reaction, which will cause a temporary quenching or damping of the solar thermonuclear process. As a result, the Sun's brilliance will rapidly decrease to about a millionth of its normal value, then recover in a period of approximately thirty minutes.

This important discovery has grave defence implications, for a potential enemy could utilize it to make a surprise attack on the United States under the cover of artificially induced darkness. It is obvious, therefore, that for its own security the US must investigate this phenomenon, and this can be done only by a full-scale experiment.

Though it is appreciated that Operation Pluto will cause temporary inconvenience to large numbers of people – a fact deeply regretted by the US Government – the defence of the Free Solar System permits of no alternative. Moreover, the benefits to science will be enormous, and will far outweigh any slight risks involved.

The numerous protests raised against the operation by many foreign scientists are ill-founded, being largely based upon inadequate information. In particular, the attacks launched by Lord Lovell of Jodrell and Sir Fred Hoyle appear to be inspired by political rather than scientific motivations. It is felt that their views would be altogether different if the United Kingdom possessed vehicles capable of carrying suitable payloads to the Sun.

As these critics have suggested that the Sun's recovery time may be of the order of years rather than minutes, a full study of the blackout process has been carried out by the Los Alamos PHOBIAC computer. This has shown that the risk of the Sun remaining extinguished is negligibly small, though the actual figure must remain classified.

Nevertheless, to explore all possibilities, the US Government has commissioned the well-known firm of independent consultants Kahn, Teller, and Strauss to make a study of the situation should the Sun fail to return to normal. Their report – to be released shortly under the title 'Economic and Other Effects of a Twenty-Four-Hour Night' – indicates that, though there may be a difficult transition period, the community will soon adapt itself to the new conditions. These may, in fact, be advantageous in many respects; for example, the enormous stimulus to the electrical supply and illumination industry would remove any danger of a recession for years to come.

The protracted absence of the Sun would also render useless the Soviet Union's announced intention of increasing agricultural production, by tilting the Earth's axis so as to move Siberia into the tropics – a proposal which has rightly aroused the disapproval of the civilized world. Should Operation Pluto have unexpected after-effects, there will, of course, be no tropics.

The United States Government, however, is confident that no such mishaps will occur, and is proceeding with the operation in full consciousness of its global responsibilities. It will not be deflected from its plain duty either by uninformed criticism, or such temporary setbacks as the recent destruction of the planet Mercury by the premature detonation of the first blackout device. This accident has been traced to a piece of chewing gum in the inertial guidance system, and all necessary steps have been taken to prevent its recurrence.

Far-fetched? I'm not so sure. For a long time, many of us have been wondering why certain types of stars occasionally blow up; and just recently, astronomers discovered an exploding *galaxy*. By the standards of the Universe, our meddling may still be pretty small-scale stuff.

But we're certainly working hard at it; and the best, I'm afraid, is yet to be.

— 22 —

Into the Abyss

The concluding section from Beyond Jupiter *(1972), the collaboration with Chesley Bonestell from which Chapters 8 and 9 are also
drawn. (JB)*

Seven or eight years after it has been boosted by the slingshot of
Jupiter's gravitational field, a Grand Tour spacecraft will reach the
known limits of the Solar System. It will still be moving under
the gravitational influence of the Sun, very slowly losing speed –
but the Sun will never be able to call it back, for it will have far
exceeded 'solar escape velocity'. When the Sun has done its utmost
to slow it down, the spacecraft will still have a residual velocity of
at least 50,000 miles per hour. At this speed, it will head out
across the interstellar gulf – toward the stars.

The nearest of the stars, Proxima Centauri, is 4.3 light-years, or
25,000,000 million miles away. If the spacecraft was aimed in that
direction, it would get there in about fifty thousand years. But by
that time, of course, Proxima would be somewhere else . . .
because all the stars are being swept along in the giant cosmic
whirlpool of the Milky Way, which turns once in every 200 million
years.

At this primitive stage of our technology, therefore, interstellar
probes are hardly practical. Even if we were patient enough to wait
until they arrived at their destinations, they could not carry
powerful enough transmitters to send back useful information from
even a small fraction of a light-year away. And it is hard enough to
build complex electronic equipment which will function reliably for
a decade – let alone for thousands of years.

Yet the idea is not fundamentally absurd; what has already been
done in the first generation of space-probing would have seemed
utterly impossible not long ago. Perhaps in a hundred years, at the

present rate of progress, we may be able to build vehicles that can reach an appreciable fraction of the speed of light. In theory, nuclear energy is quite capable of giving us this performance – and sooner or later, practice usually catches up with theory.

Such probes could reach the nearer stars in a few centuries, and a stable world-society might not think such a time scale unreasonable. (Remember the cathedral builders of the Middle Ages, planning generations ahead, in eras of plagues and wars.) And the energies that launched these far-ranging travellers would also be able to power their radio transmitters, so that they could send back to Earth the knowledge they had gathered in alien solar systems. This would indeed be a long-term research project, on a scale we can hardly imagine today. It would be as if President Washington embarked upon a scheme which could only benefit Lincoln – or Kennedy. One cannot easily imagine today's Congress voting vast sums for purely scientific projects, whose success or failure could not possibly be known before the year 2200 . . .

So perhaps it is more appropriate, at this moment of time, not to wonder when we will be attempting such feats, but to ask ourselves if other civilizations may not already have achieved them, long ago. The concept of intelligent, advanced life throughout the Universe, which until recently was seldom found outside the pages of science fiction, has become respectable with almost explosive suddenness. A number of radio astronomers have seriously suggested that we should be on the lookout for visiting space probes which may have been orbiting round the Sun, keeping a watch on the planets, for thousands of years . . .

Such probes, if they exist, would be far more sophisticated than any that we can build today; they would make STAR* seem as primitive as a Greek water clock. Because it would take years or decades for any controlling signals to reach them, they would have to be completely autonomous, able to cope with any emergency or unexpected event. In other words, they would have to be intelligent.

If we encountered such a probe, and got into communication with it, we might not be able to decide whether we were dealing with a

*This refers to a 1970 project – Self-Test And Repair computer.

form of life or with a machine. And at this level, indeed, the distinction might turn out to be altogether unimportant, if not meaningless.

All these ideas are likely to remain pure speculation for centuries to come; yet before the no-longer-distant year 2000 our own space probes will have left the Solar System. With any luck, they should continue to broadcast back information for years; just how far we can track them depends on the size of the ground-based radio telescope used to receive the signals. The 210-foot dish of the Deep Space Network should be able to follow the Pioneers out to several times the distance of Pluto. But if we used the great 1,000-foot dish of the Arecibo Observatory in Puerto Rico, the range would be increased five-fold perhaps to fifty or a hundred *billion* miles. Unfortunately, such huge and expensive instruments will always be busy on so many programmes that they cannot easily be diverted to other projects.

We do not know what we may find in the regions between the stars. Yet every time we have sent ourselves, or our instruments, into new territory, we have made unexpected and important discoveries. Before the Space Age dawned, astronomers were quite sure that there was nothing between the planets, except occasional meteors. Today, we look upon interplanetary space as a region of great activity – swept by the tenuous million-mile-an-hour gales of the solar wind, pervaded by magnetic fields, lashed by invisible radiations . . .

The late C. S. Lewis, with whom, as I mentioned earlier, I had a long and friendly disagreement about the desirability of man's escaping from his world, was much more accurate than the scientists of his time when he wrote in *Out of the Silent Planet*, back in 1938:

He had read of 'Space'; at the back of his thinking for years had lurked the dismal fancy of the black, cold vacuity, the utter deadness, which was supposed to separate the worlds . . . Now the very name 'Space' seemed a blasphemous libel for this empyrean ocean of radiance in which they swam. He could not call it 'dead', he felt life pouring into him from it every moment.

As they leave the outskirts of the Solar System, our first short-range interstellar probes will observe the diminution in the Sun's influence – the fading of its magnetic and gravitational fields. At the same time, they will be able to measure the phenomena of the Greater Universe, which until then will have been masked by the effects of the Sun and the planets. They will be able to take the pulse of the Galaxy itself, detect the onrushing debris of exploding novas, look for the dark, dead stars which, some think, may be even more numerous than those that shine.

Some time in the twenty-first century, at some indefinite distance from the Sun, we will lose contact as the power of their signals weakens – though occasionally, when some giant new telescope is brought into operation, they may be momentarily reacquired. But one day their transmitters will fail, and they will be lost for ever.

Or perhaps not; there are two other possibilities. As our space-faring powers develop, we may overtake them with the vehicles of a later age and bring them back to our museums, as relics of the early days before men ventured beyond Mars. And if we do not find them, others may.

We should therefore build them well, for one day they may be the only evidence that the human race ever existed. All the works of man on his own world are ephemeral, seen from the viewpoint of geological time. The winds and rains which have destroyed mountains will make short work of the pyramids, those recent experiments in immortality. The most enduring monuments we have yet created stand on the Moon, or circle the Sun; but even these will not last for ever.

For when the Sun dies, it will not end with a whimper. In its final paroxysm, it will melt the inner planets to slag, and set the frozen outer giants erupting in geysers wider than the continents of Earth. Nothing will be left, on or even near the world where he was born, of man and his works.

But hundreds – thousands – of light-years outwards from Earth, some of the most exquisite masterpieces of his hand and brain will still be drifting down the corridors of stars. The energies that powered them will have been dead for aeons, and no trace will remain of the patterns of logic that once pulsed through the crystal labyrinths of their minds.

Yet they will still be recognizable, while the Universe endures, as the work of beings who wondered about it long ago, and sought to fathom its secrets.

— 23 —

Predictions

Reprinted from The Book of Predictions, *edited by David Wallechinsky, Amy Wallace and Irving Wallace (1980). It is interesting to see that some predictions have not quite made it on time – but it is better to be an optimist than a pessimist. Each attitude may result in a self-fulfilling prophecy.*

Many years ago, in the opening words of *Profiles of the Future*, I stated: 'It is impossible to predict the future, and all attempts to do so in any detail appear ludicrous within a very few years.'

Strictly speaking, the very concept of a prediction is logical nonsense, because it's a statement about the future – and how can one make any meaningful assertions about something that doesn't exist? (What colour are a unicorn's eyes?) The best that can be done – and sometimes even this is a very poor best – is to outline the entire spectrum of possible futures and to assign probabilities to each item. This is not *prediction* but projection, or *extrapolation*; there is a profound difference between the two, which many people find hard to understand. Let me give an example.

If I said that the population of the United States on 1 January 2001 would be 236,453,328, that would be a prediction – and it would be wrong (barring fantastic luck!). However, a statistician might say that the population of the US at that date has a 90 per cent chance of being between 220 and 240 million. That would be an extrapolation, and if he were good at his job, he'd have a fair chance of being right. He would have taken the existing birth, death, immigration and emigration rates; made reasonable guesses about their future values; and done some arithmetic. But this procedure assumes that history won't produce any surprises, which it invariably does. The population of the US in 2001 might be only a couple of million, if there had been a nuclear war. And if you think there's no possibility of a similar error in the other direction, consider this science-fiction scenario: When the King(!) orders the multiple cloning of everyone named Kennedy, the population jumps in one year from 230 million to 1,000 million plus.

So, having proved the impossibility of prediction, here are my extrapolations, in the areas where I feel I can speak with any authority. I have given dates only to the nearest five years; anything else would be to convey a misleading impression of accuracy.

Most of the headings are self-explanatory, and I have omitted the two most important of all – the detection of extraterrestrial life and the detection of extraterrestrial intelligence. Either could happen tomorrow – or a thousand years from now. We have no hard facts on which to base even a guess, still less a *reasonable* extrapolation.

1985

* Permanent space station similar to Skylab, but in a higher orbit; carries 5–10 men.

* Electronic tutors. These will be the erudite descendants of today's computer toys – completely portable, cheap, capable of giving programmed instruction in almost any subject at any level of difficulty. They could trigger an educational explosion (particularly in developing countries) which could boost mankind out of the Stone Age.

1990

* Return to the Moon.

* Wrist telephones. These will become possible with the construction of very large communications satellites and will start a social-economic revolution as great as that produced by the telephone itself a century earlier.

1995

* Lunar base established. The beginning of planetary colonization – the main theme of the twenty-first century.

2000

* Commercial fusion power. Era of cheap energy dawns.

2005

* Manned flight to Mars.

2010

* Space cities.

2020

* Mars base.

2030

* Manned exploration of the Solar System. First robot interstellar probes.

— 24 —

Of Space and the Spirit

This first appeared in book form in The Challenge of the Spaceship *(1960).*

Astronomy is the oldest of the sciences, and the one which has not only the widest popular appeal but also the most profound philosophical implications. This was never more true than at the present time, when the horizons of human knowledge are not so much expanding as exploding. New discoveries and techniques – such as the development of electronic instruments, the launching of artificial satellites, the detection of radio waves from space – have invigorated the whole science and shed new light on problems over which men have argued in vain for centuries.

Yet what has already happened is merely the prelude to far more startling events. In a period which will be very short by the standards of history – perhaps a century at the most – we may have established physical contact with all the major solid bodies in the Solar System. A landing on the remotest of the Sun's planets may now be nearer to us in time than the Battle of Gettysburg.

The shadow of these coming events already lies across our age, stirring the thoughts of all men who have ever stared at the night sky and wondered what part our race is destined to play in the unfolding drama of the Universe. Many of the great questions of religion and philosophy must now be reformulated, and there is more than a possibility that some which seemed forever beyond hope of solution may soon be answered.

Whether intelligent life exists outside the Earth is, perhaps, unique among these problems in its intellectual and emotional appeal. The only type of life which we can imagine without losing ourselves in biological fantasies must be planet-based, and until a short time ago astronomers felt reluctantly certain that planets were exceedingly rare phenomena. Indeed, they were regarded as the results of cosmic accidents that could occur only a very few times in the entire history of any well-conducted universe.

Today we are fairly confident that the exact reverse is true; modern theories of the formation of the Solar System suggest that many, if not most, stars must have planets revolving around them. This outlook was given considerable support by the detection, in 1942, of a hitherto unknown body – much too small to be a Sun – in the double-star system 61 Cygni.* This binary star is one of our closest neighbours; it would be a most remarkable coincidence, if planets were indeed rare, to find a specimen practically on our doorsteps. If we eliminate systems which, through the instability of the central sun or for some other reason, seem unpromising as the abodes of life, we may not be far from the truth if we guess that one star in ten possesses at least one planet upon which life could theoretically exist.

This leads us to the second and equally remarkable transformation which the last ten or fifteen years has brought. As recently as 1947 it was possible for du Nouy, in his widely read book *Human Destiny*, to maintain that living things could not possibly arise from 'dead' inorganic matter by the operation of purely natural forces. The complexity of even the simplest single-celled organism was so enormous that to expect atoms of carbon, hydrogen, oxygen and the rest to form it by spontaneous aggregation was much less probable than that Eddington's famous army of simian typists should produce the entire works of Shakespeare at the first attempt. Life's appearance on Earth (or elsewhere) must therefore have been consciously directed and controlled by some organizing force, which it was tempting to identify as the hand of God.

We now know, thanks to the work of such biologists as Bernal and Oparin, that this apparently convincing argument is wholly fallacious, and that life can probably evolve from non-living matter in the circumstances that must exist upon many primitive, newly formed planets. The process may, indeed, be inevitable when we are dealing with astronomical time periods; the idea that life on this planet is some kind of freak or special creation has vanished with the

*This 'discovery' was later discredited – but several more recent ones seem better established.

belief in the uniqueness of the Solar System. Stanley Miller's famous experiment at the University of Chicago in 1952, when a complex organic soup was produced by the action of electrical discharges upon simple solutions of carbon dioxide, ammonia, methane and other gases, suggests how the first steps in the evolution of life may have taken place. (For an entertaining and not-too-technical account of the way in which the chemicals of life may build themselves up from elementary substances, see the essay 'The Unblind Workings of Chance' in Dr Isaac Asimov's book *Only a Trillion*.)

That both planets and living creatures are common throughout the universe must, therefore, now be taken as highly probable, though it cannot yet be proved beyond doubt. We may be hopelessly conservative if we guess that life may be associated with one star in every hundred. Dr Harlow Shapley, in his book *Of Stars and Men*, reduces the figure to one in a trillion by being deliberately ultra-pessimistic; he considers a more reasonable estimate to be one in a million. But any figure is, at the present stage of our semi-ignorance, pure guesswork; let us for the sake of argument settle on that one in a hundred, and see where it leads us.

It implies the existence of a billion life-bearing worlds in our single Galaxy – the whirlpool of stars of which our Sun is an undistinguished out-of-town member, lying in one of the remoter spiral arms. And within the range of our telescopes there are approximately a billion other galaxies.

Now a billion is a number all too familiar in today's budgets and military estimates, but this does not mean that anyone can visualize it. Should you feel like trying, I recommend this simple and highly instructive experiment.

Go down to the nearest beach and collect a bucketful of sand; then bring it home and empty it on the table. You now have in front of you – assuming that the sand is of reasonable fineness – something like a billion separate particles. Sift them through your fingers; each is a distinct entity, different from all its companions. How long would it take you to examine every clearly visible individual in the quite small pile before you? Devoting one minute to each, and working eight hours a day, it would keep you busy for almost six thousand years – the whole span of human history.

That is what a billion means; and now try to imagine that every one of those grains of sand is itself a world, perhaps teeming with life, and perhaps bearing rational creatures who measure their history not in thousands but in millions of years. If you succeed, you have a faint mental picture of our Galaxy; if you wish to visualize the whole observed Universe, however, the operation must be repeated with each grain of sand now representing an entire galaxy.

There is a temptation, when brainwashed by such numbers, to argue that these astronomical vistas are of no practical importance, since we can never have direct knowledge of more than a small – indeed, relatively submicroscopic – portion of the Universe. A similar policy was adopted by those followers of Aristotle who refused to look through Galileo's telescope and to see for themselves that Jupiter, as well as Earth, had moons revolving round it. If they could not be seen by the naked eye, these gentlemen argued, the heretical satellites did not really exist.

However, we cannot pretend that the Universe isn't there, for our own children will be starting to explore it, and even their first modest voyages will completely transform our view of the Cosmos. Once we can climb the mere hundred miles or so which separate us from space, and thus establish satellite observatories beyond the murk and haze of the atmosphere, it will be like emerging from a fog into the light of day. *Without travelling any further from Earth than Washington is from New York*, we will have broken through the vision barrier and will be able to view Mars, for example, from an apparent distance of only a few thousand miles. With the telescopes which we will be able to construct and operate under the perfect seeing conditions in space, we may even be able to look for the planets of other suns.

It is obviously impossible to anticipate the discoveries which will be made when we succeed in escaping from Earth; indeed, one characteristic of most really important discoveries is their unexpectedness. At the moment the astronomical evidence suggests that we will find some sort of life in the Solar System (on Mars, almost certainly;* on Venus, just possibly) but that we will not encounter intelligence. It would be rather too much to hope that

---

*No longer! But the jury is still out – we have only explored a tiny fraction of the planet, and we now know that Venus is far too hot for liquid water to exist.

two intelligent races should exist in the same small region of space and at the same moment of time.

The discovery of any form of life, however humble, on the planets would greatly affect our outlook upon the Universe by changing what is now a surmise into a certainty. Even a few lichens on Mars or a few amoebae in the (still hypothetical) seas of Venus would prove that life is not a rare disease that happens to have attacked the planet Earth. And with that settled, it would be illogical to deny the existence of higher forms elsewhere.

It is just possible that we may find direct proof of this on Mars; even if we have missed the Martians by a few million years, their records will still be written in the rocks of an arid world which knows none of the erosion or the interchange of land and sea which has obliterated so much of our own planet's remote past. But all this is pure, unfounded speculation; until we have reason to believe the contrary, it would be safest to assume that *Homo sapiens* is the only intelligent creature yet to have evolved in the Solar System. To find our equals or our peers, we must go further afield to the planets of other suns.

This, to put it mildly, presents problems. Though we are now about to challenge interplanetary distances, the gulfs separating us from the stars are a million times greater, and light itself takes years to span them. Nevertheless, there are good reasons for thinking that interstellar travel will ultimately be attainable, and round trips to the nearest stars would take about ten years. Though tedious, this would not be out of the question even for manned vessels; such techniques as suspended animation, or the use of purely automatic exploring vessels, would extend this range indefinitely.

Nor need physical transportation be necessary. With today's electronic techniques stretched to the utmost, we could just about get a readable Morse signal to the nearest star. It might therefore be worth while, as soon as we can establish satellite listening posts well away from the radio racket and electrical interference of Earth, to begin a search for intelligently modulated signals from space. If we can tackle interstellar communication only sixty years after we have invented radio, it is not unreasonable to assume that there may be transmitters within a few light-years of us far more powerful than any we have yet built. Even today, many of our radars must far outrange the Solar System – though we can be thankful that all our commercial radio programmes will have faded far below the level of cosmic noise before they can affront any stellar neighbours.

By one means or another, therefore, we may hope to establish the existence of extraterrestrial intelligences before many more decades – or at most centuries – have passed. If anyone still feels doubtful of this, I would remind him of the unfortunate error of Auguste Comte, who rashly proclaimed our eternal ignorance concerning the composition of the stars. The speed and thoroughness with which the spectroscope refuted him is a good reminder that there are no apparently fundamental limits to knowledge which may not be transcended by new techniques or inventions.

Keeping this in mind, it is not premature, and it is certainly stimulating, to consider what effect these undoubted but still unknown revelations will have upon the minds of men. They will certainly accelerate a process which has been gaining momentum since Copernicus dethroned the Earth from the centre of creation and started it upon its still-continuing journey to the periphery of the Universe. Today, it is difficult for us to believe that as recently as the time of Shakespeare no one knew that other worlds existed; though the Greeks had surmised it, there was no direct proof until the invention of the telescope *circa* 1608, and so to almost all educated men up to a dozen generations ago, our planet was the Universe. One might even say that this was still true, for 90 per cent of the human race, until the morning of 4 October 1957.

The expansion of the time scale has had equally striking effects on human thought. Until well into the last century much of the Western world believed in the literal truth of Archbishop Ussher's date for Genesis – 4004 – which may still be found printed in some bibles. It is indeed curious that so many devout men, during the three hundred years between Galileo and Darwin, stubbornly refused to recognize the grandeur of the Universe in space and time – almost as if determined to disparage the power of God. The Eastern religions avoided this mistake, which has done so much to weaken the prestige of Christianity; the Hindus, for example, take it for granted that the world's history stretches back through aeons of time that quite dwarf the few billions demanded by the astronomers.

As mankind's modest place in the scheme of the Universe is more and more widely recognized – on the emotional as well as the intellectual level – the effects on our racial pride will certainly be profound. To the Psalmist's question, 'What is Man, that Thou art mindful of him?' the future may well give the ironic answer, 'What, indeed?' Our species has come into existence in the last five-thousandth of the Earth's history, and the entire span of human civilization extends for barely a millionth of that time. Unless we exhibit a conceit which can be aptly termed astronomical, we must assume that there are many, many races in the Universe far more advanced than ours intellectually as well as spiritually. Indeed, the extreme youth of *Homo sapiens* on any cosmic time scale makes it likely that the vast majority of rational extraterrestrial creatures must be superior to us by millions of years of development.

This prospect has been viewed with some alarm by many Christians, who find it hard to reconcile the existence of other intelligent races with the doctrines of Incarnation and Redemption. If God made man in His own image, what of all the other creatures who must be made in different images, if they are to survive on alien worlds? And if Christ has saved us alone, what have we done to merit such special treatment?

During the last few years these problems – which once seemed quite as abstract as the classic question of the number of angels who could dance on a pin – have engaged several theologians. In his book *Existence and the Christ*, Professor Paul Tillich ponts out that the Incarnation preached by Christianity is for mankind only, and that other races may have other incarnations. This idea was also expressed many years ago by Alice Meynell in her poem 'Christ in the Universe':

> in the eternities
> Doubtless we shall compare together, hear
> A million alien Gospels, in what guise
> He trod the Pleiades, the Lyre, the Bear.

Tillich goes on to conclude: 'The manifestation of saving power in one place implies that saving power is operating in all places. The expectation of the Messiah as the bearer of the New Being presupposes that God loves the universe, even though in the appearance of the Christ he actualizes this love for historical man alone.'

Undoubtedly the most stimulating writer on these matters was C. S. Lewis, professor of literature at Magdalene College, Cambridge University. In two famous novels, *Out of the Silent Planet* and *Voyage to Venus (Perelandra)*, Lewis developed the theme that only humanity has fallen, and that the creatures on other planets are free from the guilt which requires our redemption. This view of mankind's peculiar depravity, well justified by a glance at the daily papers, implies that our planet is under quarantine; in the April 1958 issue of the *Christian Herald* Professor Lewis made it clear that he regarded with some disfavour our current attempts to evade this quarantine. 'Let us,' he remarked, 'thank God that we are still very far from travel to other worlds.' Unless one considers twenty-five years a very long time, this statement must now be modified to read 'travel to other worlds *inhabited by intelligent beings*'.

Another possibility, but one so flattering to our racial pride that it is hard to believe it can be true, is that the redemption of other races will proceed through us – that we, in fact, may one day take salvation to the stars. Remembering how 'gun and gospel' have been combined in the past, and the manner in which so many missionaries have attempted to 'civilize the natives', Lewis was not at all happy about this prospect. 'Would our missionaries,' he asked, 'recognize an unfallen race if they met it? Would they continue to press upon creatures that did not need to be saved that plan of Salvation which God has appointed for Man? Would they denounce as sins mere differences of behaviour which the spiritual and biological history of these strange creatures fully justified?'

Anyone who has read accounts of past mission activities (Bradford Smith's *Yankees in Paradise* is an excellent example) will appreciate the force of these questions, and Lewis argued nobly: 'We must stand firm against all exploitation and all theological imperialism . . . Our loyalty is due not to our species but to God. Those who are, or can become, His sons, are our real brothers even if they have shells or tusks. It is spiritual, not biological, kinship that counts.' In applauding these sentiments, one can also wish that they were better applied on Earth.

The Catholic Church has already accepted and welcomed the coming of the Space Age. (Perhaps the outstanding role that Jesuit scientists have played in astrophysics has something to do with this.) In 1956, the International Astronautical Federation held a congress in Rome and heard a lengthy and learned address from Pope Pius XII in which he expressed the view that now that man has discovered the means of exploring the Universe, God clearly intends him to use it. This is a ruling which most men, whatever their beliefs, will surely accept. Any path to knowledge is a path to God – or to Reality, whichever word one prefers to use.

We may conclude, therefore, that any fears that space exploration will shatter the bases of existing religions are unfounded. Nevertheless, the tremendous flood of new knowledge which will accrue from space travel (and which indeed is already flowing down from today's satellites) will in due course profoundly modify our philosophical and religious beliefs. Anyone who doubts this need only glance at the overwhelming impact of science upon faith during the past few centuries; the now settled controversies over the Earth's movement round the Sun and the evolution of man are the classic examples. Even in the last hundred years, many beliefs passionately held by the leaders of the great religions have ceased to be accepted by their equally devout successors. It would be absurd to imagine that this process will come to an end just at the moment when science is about to make the greatest breakthrough in all history.

At this moment in time, at the very beginning of the centuries-long gold rush into ever richer, ever expanding fields of knowledge, we must realize that there is no hope of understanding our Universe until we have examined a fairly large sample of it – certainly a good deal more than one small planet out of billions. Though this cautious attitude may disappoint many who are hot for certainties, any other policy would be utterly naïve. It would put us in the same position as Pacific islanders who have never yet had any contact with the world beyond their coral reef, yet who attempt to construct a picture of the whole Earth and its peoples from the view they get from the top of their highest palm tree.

Harlow Shapley, in the already mentioned *Of Stars and Men*, looks forward to our present 'anthropomorphic religions and philosophies, which have so often been conspicuously earth-bound and much tangled up with the human mind and human behaviour' expanding to embrace these new revelations of science, adding that 'a one-planet deity has for me little appeal'. The British astronomer Fred Hoyle, in the controversial series of radio talks which became the well-known book *The Nature of the Universe*, took an uncompromisingly materialist view which caused much heart-burning and ink-slinging among his listeners. He concluded that there is no evidence for the existence of God in the Universe around us, religion presumably being an illusion of the human mind.

On this view, it must be assumed that when we contact superior extraterrestrial intelligences we shall find that belief in a supernatural order of things marks an early stage of development amongst most rational creatures, and perishes with the rise of science. Most disconcerting of all would be the discovery that man alone is a myth-making animal, forever impelled to fill the gaps in his knowledge by fantasies. (Yet if this be the price we have had to pay for the whole realm of art, which is always an attempt to create the non-existent, we need not be ashamed. We will be better off than beings who possess all knowledge, but know nothing of poetry and music.)

Whatever the outcome of our discoveries and adventures in space, the fact will remain that the real Universe is more miraculous than any miracle. And even if every man now alive, seen from a century hence, appears no more than 'a savage suckled in an outworn creed', that will leave God precisely where He has always been, if He is anywhere – back at the beginning of creation, x billion years ago. (As of today, $x = 5$. But remember Archbishop Ussher.) Perhaps when God reached zero of the cosmic countdown, He turned His attention elsewhere, knowing that His work with us was done. It will certainly not diminish His glory – rather the reverse – if we discover that, in all the ages since time began, He has never tinkered with the mechanism of the Universe. Only an unskilled craftsman is forced to make perpetual adjustments to his handiwork; the real expert packs his tools and walks away when the job is done . . .

Let us, therefore, wait in a spirit of expectant humility for whatever light the future may throw upon these great questions, remembering that our intellectual sincerity may well be judged by our lack of apprehension. No honest man was ever afraid of the truth.

Faiths come and go, but Truth abides. Out there among the stars lie such truths as we may understand, whether we learn them by our own efforts, or from the strange teachers who are waiting for us along the infinite road on which our feet are now irrevocably set.

— 25 —

'Dear Sir . . .'

From Voices from the Sky, *Victor Gollancz, 1966*

One of the occupational hazards of authorship, not usually regarded as a high-risk profession, is the Letter from the Reader. I think that I can speak with fair authority on this subject, having seriously jeopardized my amateur status by publishing, at last count, 34 – oops! – 35 books,* as well as about four hundred articles and short stories. The result of this garrulity is a fine collection of foreign stamps and a thick file of letters from every part of the world, including the South Pole. Some of these letters have not been easy to answer, or even, for that matter, to read.

And I do answer them, for I feel that anyone who troubles to write to an author deserves the courtesy of a reply. However, it is a brief one, for I have long been haunted by the fate of the late H. P. Lovecraft. In case you have never heard of him, Lovecraft was a talented fantasy writer of the 1920s, who slowly starved to death while conducting a gigantic correspondence of thirty-page letters with about a hundred friends and acquaintances. He probably would have starved to death anyway on half a cent a word; but I have no intention of repeating his tragic error, and it is rare for my replies to extend beyond one paragraph.

In most cases, no more is necessary. Requests for autographs, corrections of errors (invariably, of course, the fault of my secretary or the printer), gratuitous information – a bare acknowledgement is sufficient for these. A little more thought is required to deal with one recent – as far as I'm concerned – phenomenon: the class assignment. I occasionally get a batch of letters beginning: 'Miss Jones, our English teacher, has asked us to write an esssay about science fiction, and has suggested that you . . . ' Good for Miss

*It's now coming up to eighty . . .

Jones; the only snag is that when these painfully composed epistles reach me by sea mail, at least six weeks have elapsed, and back at P. S. 473 my name is mud. So I always begin with a careful explanation of the delay, in hopes that the damage can still be undone. Every author should be extremely kind to teenage readers; they are insurance for his declining years.

Where youngsters are concerned, it is particularly difficult to deal with letters – nay, parcels – containing elaborate plans of space rockets, together with endless pages of explanation. I treat these gently, having been through the same phase myself around the age of 14. It is fairly obvious that a boy cannot compete with a design team of ten thousand scientists and half a billion dollars' worth of computers, which is roughly what it takes to produce the paperwork for a large space vehicle, and most of these hopeful plans can be dismissed as sheer nonsense at a glance. (The entire fuel tankage, for example, may be tucked under the pilot's seat where it won't be in the way.) But I should hate to discourage any future von Brauns, and all these efforts show enthusiasm, application, and the strength of mind to ignore the TV screen for several hours on end. My reply is, therefore, noncommittal as far as the specific design is concerned, but spends some time emphasizing the training and experience needed before one can do anything useful in the space field. It ends with a short list of reference books and magazines, and a few words of encouragement.

No encouragement at all is received by helpful characters who can think of brilliant stories, but just haven't time to write them down. They are prepared to hand their brain children over to me, for 50 per cent of the take.

I have yet to receive a single really worthwhile idea or plot in this way. When the concept is good, it has invariably been used before, and I pride myself on being able to say at once, 'I'm sorry, Mr Smaltz, but Sam Fink published a story about giant man-eating hamsters in *Flabbergasting Fiction* for May 1932.'

In any case, being an independent sort of guy, I hate to use someone else's ideas, even when they are both good and original. Twice in my life I have used plots donated by personal friends, and that was years ago. Gifts from strangers should be regarded with particular suspicion, for any author who accepts them may be handling stolen property. There is no certain defence against accidental plagiarism, but why increase the risk?

So far – touch wood – I have never been accused of this ultimate literary crime, but I have had one near-miss and just a few weeks ago I was shaken when another author, Poul Anderson, brought out a story on a theme which I fondly believed I was the first to develop. Much more remarkable, we had both concocted the same non-existent word – sunjammer – for the title. This in itself should be enough to disprove any charges of plagiarism (no thief is *that* stupid), but it is just as well that the stories appeared simultaneously.

As for the near-miss, almost ten years ago I made this brief entry in my little black notebook: 'Plague of indecent cloud formations.' I would have bet any reasonable sum that this idea was unique to my own dirty mind; imagine my utter astonishment in discovering that Philip Wylie had got there first.

These examples have made me all the more determined to refuse pleas from budding authors to read their stories and offer criticism (by which, as Somerset Maugham remarks, they really mean praise). Quite apart from the time and effort that this would involve, I could never be sure that, years in the future, my subconscious might not dredge up some item from an otherwise long-forgotten manuscript. Then the indignant author might rush into print, or court, and would be able to prove that I'd stolen the only good idea he ever had.

Perhaps the most unusual offer I ever received from a reader was the loan of his name. He would be very happy, he said, to appear as a character in one of my stories. I accepted the gift with enthusiasm, explaining that I'd been completely stuck over the name of an interplanetary beatnik who made a living smuggling narcotic baby food from Mars to Earth. However, as the writer did not return the legal clearance forms I sent him, the project got no further.

One mail-borne menace against which I have never developed an adequate defence is that famous American invention, the questionnaire. It is particularly insidious when it asks interesting questions, because then I feel a compulsion to answer them. ('What writer has had the greatest influence on you?' 'Which do you consider your best book?' 'What treatment would you recommend for literary critics?' 'Can an author overcome the handicap of a normal sex life?' etc., etc.) The trouble with questionnaires is that when a professional writer starts to take himself apart, he may not be able to put the pieces together again. He risks the fate of the centipede in the poem, who was asked to explain his method of locomotion, and thought so hard that he ended up 'distracted in the ditch, considering how to walk'.

All authors are afflicted by a certain amount of crackpot mail and, considering the sort of stories I write, my share of it seems surprisingly low. I have never had a letter from Napoleon; and though I have had two or three from God, there have been none – rather disappointingly – from His opposite number.

At luckily rare intervals there will be a handwritten, or horribly typed, thesis on gravity or cosmology, with a letter informing me that the writer has spent ten years developing his revolutionary new theory, which finally explains the whole Universe. As he can't get 'orthodox scientists' to listen to him, he pays me the dubious compliment of assuming that I will.

I never attempt to argue with these people, even when I go to the trouble (which is seldom) of reading their effusions. These are almost always scientifically illiterate, full of fallacies that one could no more explain to their benighted authors than one could teach calculus to a chimpanzee.

The wasted effort involved in these products is sometimes horrifying to contemplate, and I cannot help wondering how these unfortunate people's friends and relatives are affected by their activities. This struck me forcibly some years ago, when I received a letter from a gentleman who was convinced that the Earth was shaped like an inner tyre, and had a photo of a model that proved it. With the total irrelevance which is so typical of cranks, he also enclosed a photo of his wife and three little daughters. They looked a perfectly delightful family, but I would hate to take any bets on their future happiness. On the other hand, it might well be that father's harmless insanity kept him from a harmful one. Crackpottery may be a useful escape mechanism. I hand this thought over to the psychiatrists – who will doubtless dismiss it as a crackpot idea.

How to deal with letters of this type? Well, I have a series of answers, graded according to circumstances. Once again, they never run to more than one paragraph, even if they are in reply to fifty pages of minute handwriting and an acre of diagrams. They are careful to avoid criticism, and even more careful to avoid the slightest degree of encouragement. A typical specimen is:

> Dear Sir,
> Thank you for your letter and enclosures, which I have examined with care. It is obvious that you have spent a great deal of time on this project, and I regret that heavy pressure of work will not allow me to comment upon it at length. I think it may be of interest to Dr Isaac Asimov, whose address is . . .
> Yours faithfully,

This usually ends the matter as far as I am concerned, but that brave try at sabotage in the last sentence has so far failed completely. The competition is still six books ahead.

Occasionally something a little more drastic in the way of evasive action may be necessary – as when, for example, the writer informs me that his thirty-thousand-word explanation of the rings of Saturn, the tides, the weather, and the rise and fall of the stock market is merely a prelude to the full five-volume work, just waiting to be mailed to me. Then I take the coward's way out, and the writer gets this:

> Dear Sir,
> This is to acknowledge your letter to Mr Clarke. I will bring it to his notice as soon as he is again permitted to deal with his mail.
> Yours faithfully,
> Pauline de Sylva
> (Secretary to Mr Clarke)

This leaves the correspondent completely up in the air, not knowing whether I am being sobered up from the DTs, serving a jail sentence, or undergoing electroshock therapy. It never fails to work.

Exceptionally long and tedious letters get the classic treatment: 'Dear Sir, You may be right. Yours faithfully . . . ' And I am still keeping in reserve, for a suitable occasion, a reply once made in the House of Lords: 'I am indebted to you for demonstrating that there is no such thing as unutterable nonsense.'

Very effective is the phoney technical answer, which may run like this:

> Your treatment fails to explain the well-known fact that the locus of the contravariant tensor has non-commutative divergence in the region of the transfinite singularity. A simple extension of your theory leads at once to the obviously fallacious conclusion that the polarized proton flux will result in a heuristic phase imbalance of the hypergeometric catenery, so that . . . etc., etc.

The technique of fighting fire with fire is, of course, a little risky; the letter may fall into the hands of someone who will recognize it for the utter gibberish that it is. But sometimes the temptation to reply in kind is irresistible. This is how I once yielded to it, at the height of the Flying Saucer craze:

> Dear Sir,
> You have been completely deceived; the visitors from space who landed in your back garden and informed you that they had come from the planet Ying, 50,000 light-years away, are impostors. I have definite proof that they are actually from the planet Yang, which is only 40,000 light-years away.
> > Yours faithfully,

My proudest invention, however, is a diabolical device that I call the random noise, or zero-information, letter. This is hard work, and I employ it only when a writer has been abusive, condescending, or has used insufficient stamps, thus dragging me out of bed before dawn to pay the postman some mysteriously computed excess.

The random letter has to be handwritten, not typed, and I stumbled upon the technique quite by accident when trying to interpret some notes I'd made for a story. Though the story is lost without trace, I have something that is probably more valuable. In the zero-information letter, all the neutral words are just legible, but the key ones are not. In fact, they aren't even words, but only realistic squiggles which look – at least in my handwriting – as if they ought to be words. I can best demonstrate by another example:

Dear Sir,

Thank you for your squiggly letter of 30 February, which has caused me much squiggling. It is really astonishing that you have completely squiggled my squiggle! In particular, your statement that squiggle *squiggle* is actually squiggle squiggle is certainly one of the most remarkable pieces of squiggle that I have ever squiggled squiggLE sQuiggLE TO You!! I cannot too strongly suggest that you squiggle at the earliest possible moment . . . etc., etc.

> Yours squigglishly,
> Arthur C. Squiggle

This is not as easy as it looks, since sense keeps squigglinger, creeping in if I am not careful. The aim, of course, is to leave the maddened recipient completely unable to decide whether I'm expressing enthusiastic agreement or telling him to go boil his head. The lavish use of capitals, exclamation marks and underlining strengthens the impression that I'm saying something of the utmost importance. At the same time, I leave no hope that the meaning will ever be discovered: any further communications will obviously be even less decipherable.

Increasing commitments in later years have made it difficult for me to enjoy either serious or frivolous correspondence to the extent I would wish, so I have prepared a form letter which covers most of the eventualities likely to arise. It runs as follows:

Dear Sir/Madam,

Thank you for your letter: you will understand that my mail-load makes it impossible for me to answer correspondence personally, much as I enjoy doing so. (To appreciate how the postman can stop an author from writing, see Chapter VIII, 'Fan Mail and Other Time Wasters', in Robert Heinlein's *Grumbles from the Grave*.) Still less can I supply autographs and mail back books, photographs, etc. However, I hope that this reply form will answer most of your queries, and I sincerely appreciate your interest in my work.

Biographies: *Odyssey*, by Neil McAleer (Gollancz; Contemporary Books). See also *Britannica*, *Who's Who*, *Contemporary Novelists*, *Contemporary Authors*; *Ascent to Orbit*; *1984: Spring*; *Astounding Days*.

Bibliography: Now 70+ books. See above; also *Against the Night, the Stars* (J. Hollow; Harcourt Brace Jovanovich) and *Arthur C. Clarke* (David N. Samuelson; G. K. Hall).

Rights: I NO LONGER ACCEPT COMMISSIONS. All rights are handled by:- David Higham Associates, 5–8 Lower John Street, Golden Square, London, W1R 4HA, **Phone**: (071) 437 7778 and Scott Meredith, 845, Third Avenue, N. Y., 10022, **Phone**: (212) 245 5500.

Space: There are *hundreds* of books on this subject, and many organizations dealing with it, e.g. The British Interplanetary Society (27 South Lambeth Road, London, SW8 1SZ); The National Space Society (922, Pennsylvania Ave SE, Washington, D.C. 20003.)

Manuscripts: UNDER NO CIRCUMSTANCES will I comment on MSS or story ideas. And to all those enthusiasts who send me pet theories, inventions, and plans for saving the world – sorry, but I don't have the time or qualifications to discuss them.

Advice to authors: Read at least one book a day, and write as much as you can. Study the memoirs of authors who interest you (e.g. Somerset Maugham's *A Writer's Notebooks*). Correspondence courses, writers' schools, etc., are useful – but all the authors I know were self-taught. There is no substitute for living; as Hemingway wisely remarked, writing is not a full-time occupation.

2001–2010–2061: Queries. Please re-read the three novels, plus *The Lost Worlds of 2001* and *The Odyssey File*.

Requests for help: If I responded to all the appeals I get for literary, financial, educational, etc. assistance I would have no time (or money) for anything else. It is often difficult to ignore genuine and deserving cases, but I salve my conscience with the thought that I now directly support about fifty people.

The University of Moratuwa: the Arthur Clarke Centre: All correspondence to the Vice-Chancellor or the Director, please – at Katubedde, Moratuwa, Sri Lanka – *not* to me! Thank you . . .

Arthur C. Clarke, CBE
Chancellor, University of Moratuwa,
Chancellor, International Space University

I hope that all this has not given the impression that I don't like hearing from readers. Far from it, for I must now overcome my natural modesty and admit that the great majority are straightforward letters of appreciation for the pleasure my books have given. These always receive a prompt 'thank you', carefully listing any recent titles that may have been overlooked. Such letters present no problems, and are of no interest to anyone except the sender and myself. I enjoy getting them, but do not think that it would make very much difference to my output, my style of writing, or my choice of plots if there was no feedback at all from the audience. Nor have I ever been responsive to entreaties for sequels to any of my short stories or novels; I really mean it, when I write

THE END.

Other books by Arthur C. Clarke

Non-Fiction

ASCENT TO ORBIT
ASTOUNDING DAYS
THE CHALLENGE OF THE SEA
THE CHALLENGE OF THE SPACESHIP
THE COAST OF CORAL
THE EXPLORATION OF THE MOON
THE EXPLORATION OF SPACE
GOING INTO SPACE
HOW THE WORLD WAS ONE
INTERPLANETARY FLIGHT
THE MAKING OF A MOON
PROFILES OF THE FUTURE
THE PROMISE OF SPACE
THE REEFS OF TAPROBANE
REPORT ON PLANET THREE
THE VIEW FROM SERENDIP
VOICE ACROSS THE SEA
VOICES FROM THE SKY
THE YOUNG TRAVELLER IN SPACE
1984: SPRING

with the Astronauts
FIRST ON THE MOON

with Mike Wilson
BOY BENEATH THE SEA
THE FIRST FIVE FATHOMS
INDIAN OCEAN ADVENTURE
INDIAN OCEAN TREASURE
THE TREASURE OF THE GREAT REEF

with Peter Hyams
THE ODYSSEY FILE

with the Editors of Life
MAN AND SPACE

with Robert Silverberg
INTO SPACE

with Chesley Bonestell
BEYOND JUPITER

with Simon Welfare and John Fairley
ARTHUR C. CLARKE'S MYSTERIOUS WORLD
ARTHUR C. CLARKE'S WORLD OF STRANGE POWERS
ARTHUR C. CLARKE'S CHRONICLES OF THE STRANGE & MYSTERIOUS
ARTHUR C. CLARKE'S CENTURY OF MYSTERIES

Fiction
(*anthologies)

ACROSS THE SEA OF STARS*
AGAINST THE FALL OF NIGHT
CHILDHOOD'S END
THE CITY AND THE STARS
THE DEEP RANGE
DOLPHIN ISLAND
EARTHLIGHT
EXPEDITION TO EARTH*
A FALL OF MOONDUST
THE FOUNTAINS OF PARADISE
FROM THE OCEANS, FROM THE STARS*
THE GHOST FROM THE GRAND BANKS
GLIDE PATH
THE HAMMER OF GOD
IMPERIAL EARTH
ISLANDS IN THE SKY
THE LION OF COMARRE
THE LOST WORLDS OF 2001
MORE THAN ONE UNIVERSE*
A MEETING WITH MEDUSA*
THE NINE BILLION NAMES OF GOD*
THE OTHER SIDE OF THE SKY*
PRELUDE TO MARS*
PRELUDE TO SPACE
REACH FOR TOMORROW*
RENDEZVOUS WITH RAMA
THE SANDS OF MARS
THE SONGS OF DISTANT EARTH
THE SENTINEL*
TALES FROM PLANET EARTH*
TALES FROM THE 'WHITE HART'*
TALES OF TEN WORLDS*
THE WIND FROM THE SUN*
2001: A SPACE ODYSSEY
2010: ODYSSEY TWO
2061: ODYSSEY THREE

(UK only)
AN ARTHUR C. CLARKE OMNIBUS*
AN ARTHUR C. CLARKE SECOND OMNIBUS*
THE BEST OF ARTHUR C. CLARKE*
FOUR GREAT SF NOVELS*
OF TIME AND STARS*
2001, DEEP RANGE, MOONDUST ETC*

with Gentry Lee
CRADLE
RAMA II
THE GARDEN OF RAMA
RAMA REVEALED (forthcoming)

with Gregory Benford
AGAINST THE FALL OF NIGHT/BEYOND THE FALL OF NIGHT